PLOUGHSHARES

Winter 2019-2020 • Vol. 45, No. 4

EDITOR-IN-CHIEF
Ladette Randolph

MANAGING EDITOR
Ellen Duffer

POETRY EDITOR
John Skoyles

ASSISTANT DIRECTOR
PRODUCTION & DESIGN
Allison Truj

SENIOR EDITORIAL
ASSISTANTS
Dana Alsamsam
& Sally Pigeon

ASSISTANT DIRECTOR
BUSINESS & DEVELOPMENT
Cory Bailey

EDITORIAL ASSISTANT
Elliot Phillips

MARKETING ASSOCIATE
Rikki Angelides

OPERATIONS ASSOCIATE
Lillian Dunaj

MARKETING ASSISTANT
Olivia Carey

COPY EDITOR
Carol Farash

LOOK2 EDITOR
David Weinstein

BLOG EDITOR
Ellen Duffer

SENIOR READERS
John Allen Taylor, Emily Avery-
Miller, Jana-Lee Balish,
Suzanne Reeder, Maggie Su,
& Jaime Zuckerman

ASSOCIATE BLOG EDITOR
Jessica Vestuto

INTERNS
Catherine Bai & Harper Lundine Wilmoth

READERS
Taryn Bowe | Matt Broderick | Nana Campbell | Shane Clyburn | Stephanie
Cohen | Caroline Fairey | Derek Heckman | Joshua Johnson | Lisa Ludden
| Jenna Lynch | Autumn McClintock | Caroline McCoy | Kelly Mustian |
Alejandro Perez | Lara Palmqvist | James Pollack | Elizabeth Robbins | Enzo
Scavone | Bucket Siler | Jordan Stillman | Marie Sweetman | Claire Tranchino
| Lucy Walker | Sarah Wheeler | Amber Wheeler Bacon | Lynn Wohlwend |
James Wyshynski

ADVISORY BOARD
Timothy Carey | DeWitt Henry | Alice Hoffman | Jill Ellen Karp
Ann Leary | Helen Elaine Lee | Pamela Painter | Tom Perrotta
Janet Silver | Marillyn Zacharis

Ploughshares, a journal of new writing, is guest-edited serially by prominent writers who explore different personal visions, aesthetics, and literary circles. Ploughshares is published in January, April, July, and October at Emerson College: 120 Boylston Street, Boston, MA 02116-4624. Telephone: (617) 824-3757. Web address: pshares.org. Email: pshares@pshares.org.

Subscriptions (ISSN 0048-4474): $35 for one year (4 issues), $55 for two years (8 issues), and $70 for three years (12 issues); $50 a year for institutions. Add $35 a year for international postage ($15 for Canada and Mexico).

Upcoming: Spring 2020, a poetry and prose issue edited by Tracy K. Smith, will be published in April 2020. Summer 2020, a prose issue edited by Celeste Ng, will be published in July 2020. Fall 2020, a longform prose issue edited by Ladette Randolph, will be published in October 2020. Winter 2020-21, a staff-edited poetry and prose issue, will be published in January 2021.

Submissions: The regular reading period is from June 1 to January 15 (postmark and online dates). All submissions sent from January 16 to May 31 will be returned unread. From March 1 to May 15, we read for our Emerging Writer's Contest. Please see page 254 for editorial and submission policies, or visit our website: pshares.org/submit.

Donate: Ploughshares greatly appreciates the support of its patrons. To give your tax-deductible contribution to the Ploughshares Endowed Fund, call us at (617) 824-3753 or visit pshares.org/engage/donate.

Back-issue, classroom-adoption, and bulk orders may be placed directly through Ploughshares. Ploughshares is also available as full-text products from EBSCO, H.W. Wilson, JSTOR, ProQuest, and the Gale Group, and indexed in Humanities International Index and Book Review Index. The views and opinions expressed in this journal are solely those of the authors. All rights for individual works revert to the authors upon publication. Ploughshares receives support from the National Endowment for the Arts and the Massachusetts Cultural Council.

Retail distribution by TNG Specialty, Media Solutions, Ubiquity, and Disticor Direct in Canada. Printed in the U.S.A. by The Journeyman Press.

Cover art: Jesse Mockrin, *The Picnic*, 2016, oil on linen 52 x 36 in

HONORIFIC

PLOUGHSHARES PATRONS

This nonprofit publication would not be possible without the support of our readers and the generosity of the following individuals and organizations.

FOUNDERS SOCIETY

Hunter C. Bourne III, **The Ashley Leigh Bourne Prize for Fiction**
The Green Angel Foundation, **Alice Hoffman Prize for Fiction**
Marillyn Zacharis, in memory of Robert E. Courtemanche, **John C. Zacharis First Book Award**

EDITOR'S CIRCLE ($10,000+)

Timothy Carey
Denis and Ann Leary

PUBLISHERS ($5,000+)

Jill Karp

COUNCIL ($2,500+)

Carol Davis and Joel Marcus
Robert and Fran Silverman

PATRONS ($1,000+)

Alice Byers
Craig Donegan
Lee Pelton
Tom Perrotta
Elizabeth R. Rea

ADVOCATES ($500+)

Alan Bowers
James Brophy
Patricia and Paul Buddenhagen
Peggy Shumaker and Joseph Usibelli
Trink and Ernie Schurian

FRIENDS ($250+)

Robert Bauer
James Carroll and Alexandra Marshall
Allen Mears
Janet Silver

READERS ($125+)

Philip Carter
Jim Chervenak
Jeffrey Cohen
Deborah B. Davis
Steve Gerkin
Kathleen Hill
Kristen Kish
Peter Levitt
Jill McCorkle
Hope Nisly
Joyce Peseroff
Hilda Raz
Steven Schwartz
Margaret Shorr
Natalie Simpson
Emily Skyrm
Gary Soto
Tim Suermondt

ORGANIZATIONS

Emerson College

CONTENTS

Winter 2019-20

LOOK2 ESSAY

EMERGING WRITER'S CONTEST WINNERS

POSTSCRIPTS

BEULAH AMSTERDAM
The Bear

In the dim forest cabin, a brown bear stared at me. He sniffed my suitcase. I froze.

The bear looked at me with his deep black eyes. We gazed at each other. No longer afraid of him, I felt a close connection. I watched as he explored the small, rustic room, pawing at the door mat and the bedside rug.

Exhausted from the morning's hike, I lay down on the wrinkled white sheets. The bear lay beside me, his body as long as mine. His warm energy flowed through me.

When I woke up from this strange dream, I thought of Harry, my boyfriend in my freshman year of college in 1955. He was a big bear of a man with bushy eyebrows and a head of shaggy brown hair. We met in the City College cafeteria. I was circulating a petition to reinstate my English teacher who had been suspended when he refused to answer questions before the House Un-American Activities Committee.

Harry asked me some questions and then signed the petition. After that he'd stop me and ask how the petition was going. When I learned that he was a poet, I found him attractive despite his pot belly and double chin. I looked for him in the cafeteria. He was usually engaged in a political conversation and I'd sit down and listen. Five years older than me, he was wise, knowledgeable, and articulate.

One evening, I accepted his invitation to meet for Chinese food. Over wonton soup he said, "I'm a card-carrying member of the Communist party." When I just nodded my head, he continued, "Does that bother you?"

"Why should it?"

"Guilt by association. You could get into trouble."

"I'm not worried."

"You might someday lose a job like your English professor."

"I'm a long way from that."

"In our police state, you don't know what could happen, what they could do to you."

He went on to tell me how hundreds of artists, including Leonard Bernstein, Lillian Hellman, Dashiell Hammett, and Pete Seeger had been blacklisted. Harry was incensed that Howard Fast, author of one of his favorite books, *Spartacus*, was blacklisted, his career destroyed.

Before we parted at the subway, Harry invited me to his apartment for Sunday lunch. On a sunny fall day, I found his small fourth-floor walk-up flat in Harlem. He answered the door wearing a red-and-white striped apron. I'd never seen a man wearing an apron.

"I'm still basting the ham," he said.

I was confused because he knew I was Jewish, and he was too. I avoided non-kosher foods like ham because part of me felt deeply Jewish. As a part-time atheist, I didn't believe in staying kosher. But pigs were filthy animals full of disease.

These thoughts swirled through my head as Harry opened the hot oven in his tiny kitchen. A large hunk of meat, studded with maraschino cherries and pineapple, sat in a roasting pan. Using a big spoon, he scooped up the liquid at the bottom of the pan and poured it over the meat. "It's almost done," he said.

I sipped Chianti while he made a green salad and set the table. When he took the ham out of the oven and began cutting a huge slice, I said, "That's way too much for me."

Lifting up the plate he said, "This is for my neighbor."

I followed him down the hall, where a little old lady with white hair opened her door. She beamed when she saw Harry. Wearing a necklace with a gold Jewish star, she spoke with a Yiddish accent, "You know how much I love ham."

Back in his kitchen, the ham smelled so good, and I was salivating. Harry set a plate of food in front of me. I relished the cherry and the pineapple and gingerly tasted the ham. It was juicy and sweet. I loved it.

On days I didn't have to go to my part-time job as a dental assistant, and he didn't have to drive a cab, I hung out with Harry. Sometimes he roasted a chicken or cooked meatballs and spaghetti, but he usually made us meat or cheese sandwiches. During study breaks, we'd lie down side-by-side on his bed and rest together, his embrace warm and comforting.

Harry was revising a poem about a Russian circus bear being forced to dance, jump rope, and juggle. During training, the bears were chained, caged, and hit with sticks. Harry felt that Russia was a bear beaten down by the West.

Harry lacked the passion of other boyfriends, but I cherished his presence, political views, and philosophizing. When I asked him to take me to a communist meeting, he said, "If you want to become a Communist, you must do it on your own. There are dangerous consequences."

Neither Harry nor I wanted to get married or have children. He'd be the perfect partner for me. We were comrades.

I was hungry for snuggling in Harry's warm embrace. He gave me what I never got from my mother. He became the Teddy Bear I'd never had.

He'd wanted me to stay overnight, but Mama made it clear that as long as I lived at home, I had to sleep there. I was planning to move to the Girl's Club of Brooklyn soon. Then I'd be free to spend weekends with Harry.

When he told me that he and his roommate were painting their apartment and I couldn't come over for a while, I was certain he was dropping me.

After winter break, I ran into Harry in the City College cafeteria and we started hanging out again. In March, when I moved into the Girls Club of Brooklyn, I spent most weekends with Harry. His apartment was a shocking crimson. Now when we cuddled, the crimson walls held us like a warm womb.

On a June day just after finals, Harry invited me to boat up the Hudson River to Bear Mountain State Park, forty-five miles north of Manhattan. We climbed into a large rowboat and he yanked the cord to start the outboard motor. We chugged under the George Washington Bridge.

The sun reflected brilliantly across the water. The wakes of passing ferries and freighters rocked us with waves. The motor died a few times, making it a slow ride upriver.

Large rolling hills in the shapes of camels, cows, and elephants rose above the Hudson. After several hours we saw the profile of a bear lying down, nestled along the river bank, giving Bear Mountain its name. We pulled into the dock as ferry boats left to return to the city.

Clouds collected as we hiked through forests of red maple, tulip, and oak trees. Sitting on the grass looking out over endlessly rolling hills, we ate lunch. Harry had brought bread, salami, and cheese, and we shared the last beer.

It started to drizzle as we pulled away from the dock. Rain stopped and started. The boat sprung a leak. I bailed as he steered us down the Hudson.

Rain poured in. We both bailed. The motor sputtered and stalled several times and then it totally died. Harry rowed. Thunder roared.

The sky turned black. Lightning bounced across the water and almost struck us. Torrential rain swamped our boat. I prayed and bailed, bailed and prayed. Eyes shut, I rocked and sang the *Sh'ma*, praying to the God I no longer believed in.

Icy marble balls hailed down on us. Harry lost an oar. Waves washed into our boat already sitting perilously low in the water. A yacht passed close by, and we waved our towels madly. They ignored us.

From the middle of the river, with one oar, Harry maneuvered through the deluge toward shore. If the boat sunk, we'd have to swim. I doubted I could make it. I was accepting death when I saw the George Washington Bridge. I said, "We're close to the city."

"We've got a long way to go."

I pointed up ahead, "There's the bridge!"

Harry scowled at me. "There's no bridge." He shook his head and looked at me as if I were crazy.

Moments later two ancient prophets with long white beards, dressed in flowing white robes walked across the water. One pointed to the missing oar. I knew it was a vision, but I said, "There's the missing oar." Harry grabbed it.

The prophets beckoned to me to follow them, but I wanted to stay alive and knew I couldn't walk on water. They vanished under the bridge. I decided not to tell Harry about them.

While the storm was clearing, a brilliant rainbow spanned the broad river. "What a beautiful rainbow!"

Harry growled, "There's no rainbow."

Exhausted and numb, I didn't respond. I continued to bail as I shivered and shook.

The setting sun came out as we passed under the real bridge. On the dock, Harry stood looking down at me. I thought he was going to suggest dinner, but he said in a cold tone: "You're schizophrenic." He waited for me to respond. I stood there in dumb shock.

He said, "I'm late for my party meeting," and he turned and left.

Tears filled my eyes, but I was determined not to cry as I searched for the subway entrance. Our relationship was over.

Several weeks went by. I couldn't believe it when Harry phoned me from the hospital on St. Nicholas Avenue. He'd broken his leg playing basketball. His leg was in traction. He asked me to come visit and bring him a pastrami sandwich and a cup of coffee.

I felt sorry for Harry. But I was still devastated by his deserting me on the dock. I didn't want to go see him. But I figured that he was isolated and desperate the way I'd felt as a child hospitalized with pneumonia and my mother didn't visit me. Despite my hurt, I remembered all the good meals he had cooked for me and my compassion welled up.

That summer, I was a telephone operator, so I couldn't get to the hospital during visiting hours. I had to sneak in. As I passed through the door of the hospital, I started to shake all over. Hospitals terrified me.

Scared of being caught for breaking visiting-hour rules, I walked purposefully toward the stairwell and quickly climbed the steps. Harry had told me that he was on the third floor and to walk down the open ward till I saw his raised leg.

I looked at man after man until Harry called my name. I didn't recognize him with shaggy facial hair. He looked even more like a bear.

Harry's bedside table was piled high with books, magazines, boxes of cookies, and bags of pretzels and potato chips. I set the coffee container down on the only empty spot. He wolfed down the large pastrami sandwich and pickle.

He thanked me and said that he'd called me many times since Bear Mountain, but nobody answered the phone. I believed him. Messages at the Girls Club of Brooklyn rarely came through.

I heard from Harry after he returned to his apartment but only saw him a couple of times.

Early in the fall semester, Harry surprised me when I found him waiting for me after my English class. I was lonely and missed studying with him. I walked toward him, hoping he'd invite me over after school.

After some pleasantries and thanking me for helping him during his recovery, he said, "There is something I need to tell you."

People were streaming out of class and down the corridor. "I'm engaged." He pointed to a pretty, petite English classmate standing a few feet away. She smiled up at him adoringly. I hated her.

I didn't run into Harry until six years later when I was a graduate student in Chapel Hill. I was strolling across the lush green campus when a tall handsome man called out my name.

I had no idea who this stranger was. Harry introduced himself. He was buff and slender with short hair. Even his voice had changed, become lighter. He looked more like a cougar than a bear.

He exclaimed, "What are you doing here?"

"I'm a graduate student in clinical psychology. And you?"

"I'm in the Peace Corps now. I'm here for training."

This made no sense to me. "What about your wife?"

"The marriage ended in a few months. I'm gay."

Reality shifted, transformed. Dumbstruck, I didn't know how to respond. I had to get to class and suggested that we meet for coffee and talk more then. But Harry was leaving in a few hours.

He said, "I became Catholic after I had a vision of the Virgin Mary and it changed my life." His face was glowing.

I never saw Harry again.

I still dream about bears.

Mostly Married, Alone at Night

You'd better believe that if I hadn't already tied the knot
      on these sweatpants I'd be out there in the mad brick city
            painting my lips the only red my complexion will allow,
    maybe with some heels on, I could probably find some heels
or at least borrow some, well first make some friends
      in this city that shuts itself to me like a fist and ask
           the tall ones if what they wear is approximately my size,
     and then what could possibly be in my way? Besides
sweatpants of course and also how when I open the door
      I am not outside under the trees throwing down leaves
          like grief-soaked handkerchiefs but am instead
     inside the house again, to be clear not the house where I
stay which is not the house where I live but cannot
     be, no instead the house I have made of bricks hewn
        from nostalgia mines bound solid by the mortar
    of selfish aspiration, and since it is a house made entirely from
the past and the future I can't stay there either.
      It's hard to get ready for a night out with strangers/future friends
          when you can't find lipstick or how to maintain a consistent
    presence in this dimension. Say I find the shade I need—
suddenly my lips are gone and who knows when they'll come back.
     When have my lips ever done what they should? For all I know
        they're out there now, surveying skin, working their way
    across some tattooed frontier and, since they're white,
claiming and renaming what they find. I wish better
    from them, and though ashamed will take the blame
      for what they clamp and suck, for the whiskey and head,
    the lies that were truth at the time.

JANAN ALEXANDRA

Is There Any More of That

for the ladies at Florence House

The fact of April first means nothing
other than the rent check is due

& spring or not we are all tenants of snow today
& I have no children under my apron nor angels
gracing my back & the women chew slowly
while it thickens beyond the window pane

& the fact too of a hot dog without a bun
& how it can decide the outcome of the day
because so much depends on bread

iloveyou to each, iloveyou to your breadless meat
& pink fleece, your fidelity to eating out of separate
beige bowls I will fill as many as you require & leave
untouched because desire yes I love & yes I love the keys
that hang from your tender neck & the rough stumps
of whiskers that garden your mouth

& iloveyou the bags strapped across your chest yes
this armor you sway in stuffed with oranges & toothpaste
& packets of sugar iloveyou the teeth who need to bite ice
to crunch cold & yes you can have & yes there is more
& softer still because with the need to chew comes trouble

all the while thankyou perforates the inside of my cheek
& my eyes blink themselves hot & double because when
you tell me *the burned bits / he's dead now / the fatty cuts /
the soup with a base of milk & butter / just like my mama*

is there any more of that / I can only ever say yes of course
& leave iloveyou to fatten in my hands.

MALACHI BLACK
Indirect Light

i.m. Kathleen Roche (1982-2018)

God of all comfort, close
your hand over the tract
                houses of Livingston—
lay shadow on the subdivided
land of Christmas lights
                and cul-de-sacs
and minivans—withdraw
the mortar from the bricks
                that bind the staggered
townhomes and cracked
chimneys over white-trimmed
                condominiums—
swallow the mailboxes
down into the loam beneath
                each quarter-acre
lawn—pull back the plots
of mulch and patchwork
                sod until they spill
like sewage through the streets
and brim the tunnels under
                Morristown, South
Orange, and East Hanover—
strengthen the cold, crooked
                bones that mold
the undertaker's glove
as his fingers smooth the satin
                lining of the pillows
in the caskets where the dead
lay faded as old rugs—soften
                the rocks lodged
in the subsoil for the digger's

dented spade—brighten

                        the headlights

on the hearses as they bend

down turnpike exits, leading

                        another mute

procession to the cemetery's

rusted fleurs-de-lis—ice

                        the puckered

calla lily petals in green

sympathy bouquets, raised

                        so they glint

like winter trumpets

in the echo of no sound—

                        as freezing rain

rests on the headstones

and snow falls underground—

An Optimistic Engineer

They depart in the early morning hours in a rainstorm, and as they drive north the sheets of falling water turn to windblown snow. The client leads in an SUV with a couple of his employees; Jake follows in his own SUV, Reggie beside him. Despite the weather, the client presses the speed limit, 75 mph in Colorado, 80 mph in Wyoming. Two hours. Three hours. "We're going to die," Jake says, repeatedly. "We're going to die in flames and snow." The wipers labor, and the tires carry forward on the icy lanes as if floating. In the passenger seat, Reggie sleeps. Reggie is hard of hearing. It is late May; five days ago it was 90 degrees.

Despite the specter of imminent death, it is a long drive, and Jake's thoughts stray to other depressing topics. When they finish their work today, they will spend the night in Gillette. Jake's ex-wife, Deb, is from Gillette, her father a welder and rodeo cowboy, but she moved to Denver the moment she finished high school, and she always said she loathed the wind, dust, and emptiness of Wyoming. Then, as soon as she and Jake were divorced, she moved back to Gillette. Jake notes gloomily that it would be a terrible mistake to go see her. Fiascos will ensue. Yet, of course, while he's in Gillette, he will try to see her. It's doom. But maybe she can help him with the boys. Maybe there's some tiny chance.

Reggie in the passenger seat wakes and tells a story about a compressor station that he helped design years ago, which later caught fire. "Of course, a fire starts, they just get everyone out, close the block valves, and let the place burn to the ground! Wasn't my fault, thank God! Bad relief valve!" Due to his difficulty hearing, Reggie speaks as if yelling to someone in another room.

The snow turns back to rain. Perhaps they won't die after all. And maybe it doesn't matter anyway, Jake thinks, since every day is either a slow death or a fast death. That's the only real choice. He tells Reggie—because it's necessary during this trip, and he wants to get it out of the way—that he'll probably have to shut down the office next week and file for bankruptcy. "You've said that a hundred times!" Reggie says.

This time it's absolutely true, but Jake doesn't say that. Instead he says, "The thing everyone forgets about the boy who cried wolf is that eventually the wolf did come and eat everything up."

At a gas station, they meet several men who work for the Arroyo Pipeline Company. In a convoy of SUVs, they pass over a cattle guard and proceed by gravel backroads and two-tracks into the rolling empty expanse of prairie. Eventually, they arrive at a complex of machinery on a large square of gravel. Massive engines power reciprocating compressors interconnected by steel pipes with huge vessels half buried in the earth and a 25-foot flare stack flaming at the top with a continuous ripping sound. The machines here pull natural gas from wellheads, knock out some of the liquids that come with the gas, and then push the gas on to other facilities for more cleanup, more compression, and finally to factories, power plants, homes, and kitchen stovetops.

Jake has spent a lot of time in places like this, and still it seems a miracle that it all doesn't blow up and kill him. Who knows when the relief valves were last tested? The operators mention that these engines have more than 100,000 operating hours each. They mention "deferred maintenance."

The client draws Jake away from the others. The client's name is Samuel, and Jake worked with him years ago, when they were young engineers, designing and building natural gas liquids terminals in the Four Corners area. He wants to know what Jake thinks. "What are you hoping I'll think?" Jake asks.

"I think it looks fine," Samuel says.

Samuel is brokering a deal for the sale of the Arroyo system, which consists of about two dozen natural-gas gathering stations, including this one, scattered across northeastern Wyoming, and linked with over a thousand wellheads. Samuel has investors ready to buy, and he told Jake that the deal is on a short rope, investors with money available, a seller desperate to settle debts on a fast approaching deadline. He asked Jake to do an engineering review, to provide the investors with a warm fuzzy, but the schedule allows Jake just two days onsite, which is only enough time to look at a fraction of the system; his report will have to be heavily caveated. Jake's looking at equipment, and Reggie, a piping designer, will provide a review of the piping.

"Well," Jake says. "It seems typical for the type of facility in the region."

"Meaning?"

"It's junk. Like all the other junk twenty-year-old compressor stations around here. We'll be lucky to leave alive."

Samuel claps him on the shoulder. "You're saying it's fine." Even when they were first starting out, Samuel was always the one who could make a few assumptions and leap over unknowns. That's how you get things done, he'd say, and it's true that he's been very successful. He shifted years ago from engineering into developing and brokering projects. He wears shining black cowboy boots, angular eyeglasses, and a strange watch like a tiny spaceship. He says, "I'm sure your report will be terrific."

Jake shrugs. If he were an investor he would want a more thorough report, but he's not an investor. Meanwhile, if Samuel can complete the sale, the new owners will begin to update and expand the system, and Jake's little engineering company will be in a position to get the design work. If his company survives that long. Which he doubts.

At lunch, in a little restaurant with white walls and fluorescent tube lighting, everyone orders the bison burger and iced tea. Jake goes to the bathroom and finds that some maniac with a tile saw has tiled the entire bathroom, floor to ceiling, brown tile with quarter-inch lines of gray grout. Not only the sink but even the urinal is tiled inside and out. Is there a normal, ceramic urinal hidden underneath the tile? Jake feels as if he's entering the region of Deb's influence, a zone of controlled mania. She would never have done this herself, but she would have encouraged whoever did it. It's a bad idea to see her. She always tells him things he'd rather not hear.

They drive to another gathering station, and then a third. The rain turns back to snow, huge clumped wet flakes. Jake retreats to a compressor building, a metal-sided structure where the sound of the gigantic engine is calamitous, but at least it's warm. He feigns interest in the machine's control panel. The tremendous noise is like a silence.

The disasters of his life have so many origins, dependent variables, controlled and uncontrolled factors. Despite state-level legality in Colorado, the Feds don't allow marijuana operations access to the banks. So, when Jake designed a fire protection system for a large grow-house—sprinklers, detectors, fire pump, alarm panel, fire department connections, backflow preventer—payment arrived at his office in stacks of cash in a backpack. A short time later, his two sons—Lucian and Richard, young no-accounts in their twenties—walked in. Were they here to take the cash? Obviously, they were here to take the cash. Yet, one wants to give one's offspring the benefit of the doubt. And they hadn't stolen anything from Jake recently, although they had been stealing things since elementary school. Even before elementary school, they loved fountains. Toddled straight in for the coins. Was it Jake's fault that they were this way? Should he have treated them with more kindness? More discipline?

Jake felt at fault, and the boys knew how to take advantage of such feelings.

He should have known. In truth, he did know. And yet.

Jake excuses himself early from dinner with Samuel and messages Deb. She replies: *Ya alright come on over we're home.*

He hasn't visited since she remarried, and he's not sure where she lives. He writes: *Where's your house?*

It's typical that she wouldn't reply. On the internet he finds an address. Glock Avenue. At the corner of Derringer Drive. Which, really, seems a bit much.

Glock Avenue winds into a subdivision of cul-de-sacs and newish houses with attached garages and tidy lawns. It might be the suburbs of Denver or Orlando or Boston, except that the pickup trucks here are especially large. As Jake rings the doorbell, he's aware that the internet may have misled him, that this might not be her house at all. But as soon as the door swings, he knows: this is her house. He knows by the smell, a moist confusion of animal, chemical, and woodworking, and by the dim chaotic clutter of the room before him—in the first moment, his mind cannot grasp the details, only the density of things, everywhere, in a huge room. Such grand chaos is how they would have lived, if he hadn't struggled against it all the days of their marriage, all fifteen years.

But he cannot see anyone. Who opened the door? He steps forward, and a movement draws his attention overhead—a piece of net is bolted to the ceiling, and a child clings to it, upside down, watching silently. "Hello," Jake says. "Please don't fall on me and kill me. Is Deb here?"

The child only stares, but Deb appears through a doorway across the room, three dogs bounding around her and a couple of children trailing behind. The dogs spot Jake and race to get their front paws onto his chest and lick his face, large mongrels with the friendly wagging tails of Labs. Deb calls hello, does nothing about the dogs, pokes at her phone, argues with yet another child who has wandered in. She wears track pants and a shapeless sweatshirt, a pragmatist's uniform, but Jake likes pragmatism, and she looks good. Rosy-cheeked. Confident posture. By the time the dogs will allow themselves to be shoved aside, Deb has disappeared again.

Jake waits for her to reappear. He knows how it will go. Deb always wanted to have many things going on around her, and to move calmly through them, making things right, a battleship mediating conflict among dinghies. She had, for a time, made Jake feel safe. Children and animals wander in and out of the room— dogs and cats in quantities Jake doesn't try to track. A rabbit. Birds call from another room. And he begins to understand the clutter— up and down the walls and across the ceiling are handgrips, monkey bars, ropes, sections of net, bungee cords, a bowling pin, a tennis racquet, rails, hooks, and ledges. From time to time a child leaps up and swings from one thing to another. Large foam pads lie here and there, and the children throw themselves onto these, or the sofa, or a chair. They narrowly miss the dogs and a little red-headed girl sleeping on the crash pads. "Jesus," Jake says. "How many kids have broken their necks in this place?"

"We have my three stepkids here," Deb says, for she has reappeared, right beside Jake, somehow. "And we have, what, four, no five, others in the house, friends, a cousin, for a sleepover. I think most of them are sleeping over. Necks are generally OK."

A wiry, smiling man has edged up. Deb introduces him—Darren, her new husband. He is about ten years younger than Deb, and Jake loathes him instantly. He has a tight little potbelly like a skinny woman seven months pregnant. Firm grip. "Good to meet you! Any ex of hers is an ex of mine! Ha ha ha!" He reaches, jumps, and grasps a pair of baseballs suspended from the ceiling and swings across the room via ropes and chains, throws himself to the wall, catches a ledge by his fingertips, spider-climbs around an open doorway, vanishes.

"Do you know that ninja show?" Deb says. "On TV? Darren's way into it. Way. He's training to try to get on the show. Good thing is, it keeps the kids busy too."

"I wanted to talk to you, about Lucian and Richard," Jake says.

"I've come around to your idea," Deb says. "Maybe we had them too young."

"I said that?"

"You said that all the time."

Jake can't remember ever saying it. But Deb always seems to have arrived in the present via some slightly alternate version of the past. Jake says, "That's not—"

But then a child screams somewhere deeper in the house. Deb hurries off.

Darren reappears, with a drink. Presenting it, he bows. "A beverage, sir?" It seems to be something like a vodka tonic, clear, sweet. Jake doesn't often drink alcohol, but he downs this with relief. Darren, meanwhile, does pull-ups while hanging by his thumbs. He asks why Jake is in town, and Jake explains, and Darren exclaims, "I worked two years for Arroyo! Validating wellhead meters. I know all those guys; I seen all that shit."

Deb, crossing the room while holding an icepack to a child's head, calls toward Jake, "We were too young, but we did our best!" She has taken off her sweatshirt, revealing a tank top. Jake notes her clavicles. Once upon a time, he had been obsessed with her clavicles. He wonders if she remembers. Darren fetches another drink. The children crowd around the red-headed girl sleeping on the crash pad to draw triangles and spirals on her face with purple and green markers. Strangely, Jake's drink is empty again. Darren gives him another, smiling.

Next, Jake has been explaining everything to Deb. How Richard said that, well, after all, maybe he and Lucian didn't deserve Jake's love. Jake rejected this suggestion. But, Richard said, love and trust are all gummed together. How can you have love without trust? Somehow, the brothers had maneuvered Jake outside—something about going to see Lucian's new dog. Jake didn't dare leave the backpack behind, so he took it with him. Maybe they didn't know what was in it? Maybe it was a coincidence that they were here? Like hell it was. Jake exclaimed irritably that of course he loved them.

Wanting to slow the pace of things, he sat on a park bench. A mistake. Lucian moved behind the bench and put his hands over Jake's eyes. Richard was still talking about trust. Don't take my backpack, Jake said. Richard told Jake that he needed to escape his own negativity. Jake said, Engineers are not made for optimism. An optimistic engineer is a bad engineer. An optimistic engineer says, "It'll be fine." And then people die.

Lucian's hands were warm on his face, and it was hot all around. The sun struck with the faintest hiss of crashing photons. Jake could feel his skin slowly dying of radiation damage. Richard said that he understood why Jake didn't trust them, but it had all changed. They had changed. Wasn't it true that he and Lucian had stayed out of trouble now for a long while? If their father wouldn't believe in them, who would? At some point, you have to make the leap, back to trust, to love. Richard suggested that Jake should close his eyes and count to one hundred. They would wait to see if Jake kept his eyes closed. Lucian's hands lifted away. The photons burned crimson through Jake's eyelids.

Of course, when he opened his eyes, the boys were gone, and the backpack.

"Well, they're right," Deb says. "You don't really trust anyone, do you?"

"I let them take the money!"

Deb waves this off, a little awkwardly—under one arm, she holds a cat. The cat dangles with strange forbearance. "You let them take it not out of trust but out of guilt." Deb laughs. "Mistrustful and guilty-feeling and anxious, that's you!"

"You always had the knack for making me want to kill myself." Jake finishes his drink. The thing is, at least she understands him. She knows the worst. He doesn't have to pretend or explain.

Darren rope-swings out of the kitchen and, impressively, spills only a little of the drink he carries. He hands it to Jake. "Cheers!" Jake accepts it with hatred. Darren bounces on a small trampoline built into the floor. Deb swats at a child attempting to horsey ride one of the dogs. She is saying, "We tried it your way with Lucian and Richard. We'll see what happens with these."

"We did not *try it my way*." Jake puts down his empty glass and resolves not to take another. "Would you talk to the boys for me? I think it'd mean a lot coming from you."

"How much money is this all about?"

"A lot. It's going to put me out of business. Twenty-eight thousand dollars."

Deb falls into hysterics. "I hope the boys gave you a receipt! Anyway, if you wanted your money back, you should've called the cops. That's what normal people do."

"But," Jake says, "Lucian would never survive in jail."

Deb shakes her head. "Lucian has you on a string." A sound from her phone causes her to poke at it rapidly. Darren wanders up and hands Jake another drink, which he accepts before he remembers his resolution not to. It occurs to him that Darren may not be thinking in terms of his best interests. Children fling themselves back and forth between large, slanted surfaces. The dogs lie on the floor and watch as if bored. Something crashes—a glassy, shattering sound—in another room. Deb rushes off.

At the sound of the crash, she sets her phone on the arm of the sofa. Jake eyes it. No one seems to be paying attention. The screen is locked, but Jake tries the four-digit passcode she always used, and it works. Hurriedly, he texts Richard and Lucian: "Call me pls!" He returns the phone to the arm of the sofa.

It rings about five minutes later, as Deb is crossing the room. She picks it up, glances at the screen, stops mid-stride, and turns to Jake. "It's Richard."

Jake attempts to look concerned. "You'd better answer. Probably something terrible has happened."

She says hello to the phone. After a moment she says, "My text."

"Ask him to return the money," Jake says.

To the phone she says, "Yes, actually, Jake is here."

"Please," Jake says.

"No," she says, "I don't know anything about a text message. I think there's been a mistake."

Jake groans. He feels like a paper doll being torn in half, straight down through his head. The idea of handing his children to the authorities appalls him, and surely it will end in bitterness and tragedy. But they are adults, and of course she is right, it is all that one can do. "Wait, wait," Jake says. "Tell him that he has to return the money, or we'll call the police."

She glances at Jake, startled. It is an expression that Jake prizes, it is so rare.

But she recovers, and now her look is one he has seen many times—lips set, one eyebrow up. "I won't tell him that," she says, "unless you mean it."

Jake, with terrible dread, nods.

She talks into the phone, moves through a doorway. Jake starts to follow, but she swings the door shut.

Meanwhile, Darren has been circling the room using only holds on the walls, touching neither the floor nor the ceiling. "Hey." He drops from the wall and sidles up. "But how did you get her to do that?"

The touch of ache in Darren's voice causes Jake's hatred of him to drop an increment. Still, he isn't about to admit that he broke into Deb's phone. "It was a bad idea," he says. "It'll end in disaster."

"But—" Darren grabs a rope and hangs from it, legs dangling.

"Sometimes," Jake says, "you can nudge her onto a path, and once she's on a path, she feels compelled to keep going."

"Huh." Grimacing, Darren ascends the rope a couple of feet, then comes back down. "I got a question. You don't have to answer. Whose idea was your divorce?"

How long have Deb and Darren been married? Three years? Jake asks, "What did she tell you?"

"You." Darren swings faintly side to side on the rope. "What made you decide?"

Surely, this is a bad question to answer, but Jake is curious himself what he will say. "Living with her made me so—" he struggles to find a word for the feeling, and finally settles "—tired, I guess. It's hard to keep up with her."

Darren stares. "You still love her though."

"Not like you're thinking," Jake says.

But saying it he realizes, by the pulse in his throat, that he is lying. He briefly reviews his scant relationships with women, the tidy emptiness of the house where he lives alone, and he wonders why, oh why, all his paths in life must lead to disaster and misery, failed choices, or right choices that nonetheless create a feeling of failure.

Darren drops to the ground. "You want to know what's going on with that Arroyo system," he says, "tell them to show you Roseacre Station, Beltline Station, that whole eastern end. Jesus. What a fucking mess."

Deb returns. "Richard says he'll bring you the money tomorrow night."

Jake considers this with a sinking heart.

"I don't believe him either," Deb says. "When he doesn't bring the money, you have to go to the police. Maybe then the money will turn up, and you can revoke the complaint with the police. I don't know."

Jake has to turn away. The thought of going to the police makes a roaring in his mind.

Deb, meanwhile, is still talking. She is saying, "Meth? Coke?"

"What?"

"Why else would they need that much money?" Deb says. "Figured out when you were getting a cash payment, staked out your office."

"Oh, no," Jake says. "I think they just kind of—" It begins to come to Jake, crushing his chest. "Lucian did look awfully thin." He groans. "I always think of the worst," he says, "but I didn't think of that."

"Addicts don't care," Deb says. "They'll take until you have nothing left."

Jake wakes on the sofa in the dark. Sitting up, he topples a drink into the cushions. He finds the glass and sets it on the floor. Now his pants are wet. Incredibly, all is quiet. He rises and steps on something soft; it yelps and darts away. Probing, Jake makes his way to the front door.

Outside, a black sky over a world white with snow. He steps off the porch, slips, falls—catching himself in the snow, he sees his bare hands, covered with something. Circles. Triangles. Remembering the girl asleep on the crash pad, he feels at his face.

He shuffles halfway to the car, but stops. Is he too drunk to drive? Yes. Can he sleep in the car? He thinks no. He will freeze and die as he dreams. He returns to the front door, but it locked behind him. Maybe, he thinks, he can slip in the backdoor.

A creaking fence gate. The soft shapes of children's toys beneath a layer of snow. Figures are silhouetted in a lit window overhead—Darren and Deb, arguing. Darren paces in and out of view, waving his hands. Deb is still, like a rock that Darren is breaking against, wave after wave.

Now Darren seems to be weeping. He sways. Deb hugs him to her breast. And Jake stands looking up as if at angels.

It's inevitable that the two of them will end up divorced. Darren will leave her, Jake thinks, for some relationship where he doesn't feel like a mouse beside an elephant. And what will Jake do then? He will try to win her back. It will be terrible. She will laugh and turn him away, and he will lose all hope; or they will actually try to build a relationship again, which will likely be worse.

The light goes out.

The backdoor, too, is locked. Jake stumbles into a shed, pulls a tarp over himself, curls up on the wooden floor for perhaps an hour, wondering about his boys, what he can say, what he can do, until he wakes shivering violently. He wonders if the end always comes in the shape you can see coming all along, if you look.

At the hotel, the receptionist stares. Jake scrubs for twenty minutes to remove the shapes from his hands and the cat whiskers from his face.

Everyone meets at the Arroyo company offices at 7:00 a.m. Samuel is smirking and backslapping. When he grips Jake's shoulder, Jake flinches away. It occurs to him that he never cared for Samuel and his cheerful corner-cutting. Jake goes to a map on the wall, pretends to study it for a minute, then points to Roseacre Station and Beltline Station. He announces that he wants to see them. The pipeline operators say the roads out that way are too muddy. Jake insists. The pipeline operators argue. Samuel watches with narrowed eyes. Eventually, the operators shrug and relent.

Roseacre Station is not muddy, but it is shocking. The ground has settled underneath buildings, causing them to lean, and tanks have heaved and leaked, flanges have cracked. Noxious black patches cover the earth, spreading like evil itself. By the time they straggle out to Beltline Station—equally awful—Samuel is pale and grim. He takes Jake's elbow to pull him aside. "How did you know?"

"I didn't know it was like this."

"Bullshit. You knew something, or you wouldn't have insisted."

"I didn't know," Jake repeats. "But now we know."

"Thank God," Samuel says.

Jake backs away a half-step. "Won't this kill the deal? It'll take piles of money to remediate here."

"Oh yeah. I had lined out my own funds to seed this one." Samuel looks at Jake, wide-eyed. "I would've been utterly fucked."

Jake drives home in a state of fugue and misery, second-guessing himself, regret gathering like steam on a window. He hoped to hurt Samuel, but did nothing to hurt Samuel. He has killed his own chances at future work on the Arroyo system. He did the right thing. But that doesn't matter. None of it matters. Why do we work, Jake wonders, when, if stupidity doesn't get us, then entropy definitely will.

Reggie, meanwhile, is in a good mood. He marvels that Jake knew where to go; the investors have no idea how lucky they are. He says, "We earned our pay today!"

Jake tells Reggie that he had better start looking for another job.

"Right! Sure! Really?!"

"Probably," Jake says. "Very, very likely." He's thinking maybe he can get the money back from his sons and string the company along for another month or two. He's also thinking that of course he won't get the money back from his sons.

Horse head pumps nod beside the interstate. No rain, no snow. But around Cheyenne, for twenty miles, thirty, there is fog. Jake can see little, but he barrels forward through the vanished world, guided by the white and yellow lines rushing out of the gray. He says, "I think my sons are addicts."

"That's bad! I had an uncle who was a heroin addict! He died!"

The thought takes Jake's breath away. He says, "I'm going to change my life."

Surely, that's the only thing he *can* change. But how? Jake wonders if he can, if it is possible, really, for anyone to change. Nothing changes, or everything changes.

The fog. The fog! He thinks, with a feeling like solace, that he may die in this fog, and then it will not matter.

He says again, "I'm going to change my life."

CONOR BRACKEN
Say Forgiveness

is a bone you dig out of your body
with another bone

because how else can I describe
the kind of time it takes
forgiveness to thicken inside a body

which is divided into various
half-heartedly warring nations

a dry forest waiting
for the sky to blush

a parking garage
ringed with shopping carts

this carpet of fire ants floating
over the river for as long
as they cling to one another

and the river which is steady
and lends its name to the rain
that scrambles its face

while forgiveness thickens
slowly underground like

some dumb potato
you would dig for
if you knew where it was planted

except it's not a potato

it's a bone and the spade
you're fathoming the loam
and stone and mud with

is also bone
which you've used so much
you keep needing to replace it

which is why all the birds
from the body's many scattered nations
are gone

by which I mean I am making

the silence
music needs in order to break

Contender

It's alright to overdress for the riot. Your rage is stunning.
It's alright to pursue the wrong pleasures and the right suffering.
Here's my permission. Take it. It's alright to replace a siren

with a bell. Let the emergency make some music. It's alright
that the meter reader broke your sunflower in half. You knew
better than to plant it where you did. Sometimes it's alright

if you call your waiter honey when you order sweet tea. It's alright
if you fall out of love with being alive, but try again tomorrow
with French pop songs and fresh croissants, wear all your gold

to church, and try—really try—to believe anything but a stethoscope
can hear your heart's urgency. It's alright that your mother died.
So will your father. And your son. But hopefully not before you.

It's alright to lie naked in the rain and refuse to go inside even
when the moon tries to make your cold thighs shine. It's okay
to lick the ice cream cake from your fingers. Do it. Now. In front

of everyone. And if what falls on the children lining up their cars
for the soapbox derby is not snow but ash, that's alright. Celebrate
the mutable body. And if you write notes to friends and senators

in primary colors, that's fine. It's even okay to begrudge the stubborn
pears in the wooden bowl. You're right, you know. They're waiting
to yellow until you turn away. It's alright that in the economy

of forgiveness you keep coming up one daffodil short. It's alright
if you ask your heart to grow the size of Secretariat's—not because
you want to outrun other horses or because your legs are classic,

but because you, too, want to be buried whole after someone
examines the insensible engine you left behind—iamb of the
beloved's name no longer metronoming the valves—and places

that slick fist in a stainless tray for weighing and shouts Sweet
Jesus before describing its ungodly heft with superlatives, your
heart the most tireless, wildest, wiliest, thirstiest heat on record.

STEPHEN BROWNING
Last Things

What will you write about your final day?
On that last page the words require truth's grain.

What use is one more journey's destination?
The sweet surprises of another day?

What, when the great fire roars through your home?
What, when the earth's fault slips with its sundering?

What passion can you kindle to survive them?
No, no, none will stand you in much stead.

You're here for a time, and time is—what it is.
Write this: Five senses are all we have of the world.

Relinquishment may be the only story.

FERENC BARNÁS
Another Death: ellipsis

translation by Owen Good

It's there. It's gone. Both. Almost always.

I didn't go out for four days; I was inside the entire time. I stocked up on wine. At the time, I never considered that I shouldn't, that I should do something to combat this; I forget resolutions I'd previously made during or after similar occurrences. Or I don't forget anything, I just suddenly conclude that I'm back there again, I'm back in that same space I've been guarding myself against for as long as I can remember. I don't know if guarding is the right word, but this is the reason I started a lot of things. This is how the boulevard came about. The grocery shop. The Market Hall and the long circuits too. The Westend shopping mall and the underpasses; Margit Island Park and Moszkva Square; the Danube bank, the tram stops, the daily Hajós Street-Nádor Street route and plenty of others. Not the corner shop thieves; I only go there to buy things or sometimes to return bottles. That's where I first met the bowing man, whom I didn't know at the time; I only realized it was an act later. I was queueing at the till and he was standing two behind me; he was rocking his torso back and forth, holding his hands out and shouting, "I'm hungry, I'm hungry!" I can't handle these situations. When I got to the front, I paid and hurried out the door. I didn't go home.

I live in the Breitner building, which isn't the Breitner building anymore but I'll explain that later. To the right of us is the Budapest Talmud Torah Society synagogue with the Yeshiva, to the left are the corner shop thieves whose owner has been trying to sell the shop for a while now. He still employs at least eight staff in two shifts; it's not hard to guess what sort of movement of cash is going on there. I moved into the kitchenette years ago, into one of the building's old servants' quarters, which the old lady first told me about. Not the first time we met; the first time we met unexpectedly, this person was just standing in the doorway: "Excuse me, are you the new tenant? I'm Mrs. Végh, you can call me Heddi." I seem to remember a few months later, quite out of the blue, the old lady told me what had happened in my flat once. "And I'll tell you something now, dear, she wasn't some harlot or the like, she was a seamstress, an honest and respectable seamstress. God forbid, I best not say anymore." She told me all of this on the open second floor corridor overlooking the courtyard, and it seemed like the artist was downstairs standing in front of her door.

The man with the matted hair, who hadn't always looked so worse for wear, had come up with something new: he came after me, following me past Oktogon, the Opera House, Nagymező Street corner; I often waited quietly in front of the artist's door to listen in case the man was coming up the stairs after me, in case he could have come in after me. I could never be sure he wasn't waiting in that niche in the wall. He hissed in my face like last time; I didn't want to punch him, I just made an involuntary movement which upset him. He shrugged his shoulders and I was forced to run—our bodies almost met; I couldn't tell what he would do, what he might be prepared to do. Once, he leaned into me; his mouth stank, and I clutched the longest key in my pocket between my fingers, ready for anything, but I didn't have to use it.

There are situations where we're quick to believe certain eventualities couldn't occur to us even conceptually. That's how it was with me. I listened to every piece of information the old lady thought essential in terms of the circumstances or the incident itself, information she herself only knew from the accounts of others, as I later found out; meanwhile, I concentrated on not picturing the details, which I usually did despite my wishes; afterward, I did think about it but I soon forgot the whole thing. For years, I never thought about what had happened where I live, and most likely it would have completely left my memory had I not, during my last Swiss trip, from one day to the next, got into one of *those* states. To this day I don't know what exactly happened, or whether anything even did happen, and if something did, with what or how I'd ever explain it. Perhaps I'd need to search for the cause in the events leading up to my trip, though I might have to dismiss that theory, considering what came later. One thing is certain. I'd called Michael from back in Versoix. Or rather, it was when I was home again I had the grill put in.

Spare some change for a magazine, sir? he says. Just like the other who turned up later and acted like a hooligan. That man would stand in a black sweater with a red scarf around his neck either by the old Goethe Institute or on Blaha Lujza Square, or on Moszkva Square, and peddle his latest theories. None of the Goethe staff reacted to the *faggot prick, step outside and I'll break your arm*, though the shortest waiter was near my own table next to the door. Later, I saw the same hooligan with the scarf, sticking up his self-made posters in different spots about town. X-free parliament, they said, Y-free Hungary, they went on, Z-free who-knows-what, they ended, and he printed copies and copies of the black-and-white A4 pages to which he sometimes added pictures and illustrations. And then he stuck these up anywhere he could: on trees, on walls, on anything.

I should have known I couldn't stay in the flat, it was pointless stocking up on enough wine, which in my case isn't so much, five or six bottles at most, because during the course of this state, I only need alcohol at the beginning; those minutes, quarter-hours or half-hours around the beginning, regardless of how it passes, how and in what rhythm, because often it's the rhythm that matters most, as far as I can remember, it's only later I can say or claim such a thing, never during it or straight after, I forget what it was there was, if there was anything at all, while at times, I was more clearly and more dramatically affected by chocolate, scrambled eggs, or pasta and sauce. I couldn't say now, no matter how hard I tried, I couldn't, but then that's part of it, you can't say, you're incapable of saying what it is that you're in, or even how you're in it, if you're even in it at all, because sometimes I do feel while this whole thing is taking hold of me, it's still happening somewhere else, somewhere else in relation to me, even if it affects me, while hours turn into whole mornings and afternoons and you make no progress, not as if here there exists any way of knowing what's progress from what's not progress; the same thoughts over and over, always the same, and for a rare moment when you think you're free of it, it's still there, it's inside, becoming a part of you just like you never wanted.

I would guess the window of my room is at least fifteen meters from the ground, and if I look out of it, I can see the back courtyard, where yellowy-gray flagstones cover almost 80 square meters with an iron drain in the middle. I remember he was a Greek man. No. He was Bulgarian, or better put he was of Bulgarian origin, his name was something like Vaszev or Vaszerev. He spoke remarkably eloquently and asked several times if I was certain I wanted a grill installed over the window. No one's going to be scaling that wall, trust me, check for yourself from the neighbor's! I mumbled something, at which he went on, saying, please, just tell me, this high up, why, tell me, what for? I didn't answer. After a short pause, he asked for the last time if I was quite certain, to which I answered, yes, I'm certain. And he started working. For a while, he didn't know how he would get at the wall behind the frame, getting at it would be more than onerous, he said, and turned to me. "Getting at it is always impossible in places like this," he said. But eventually, he worked out the technique. He drilled the holes and inserted the wall plugs, and by early evening he was screwing the grill up in six places. When I paid him, he looked at me and said, "It'll be like a hospital room."

I didn't go out for four days, perhaps only three and a half, it doesn't matter how long; if it did matter at all if it was four or three and a half, last week, this week, or any week, it wouldn't matter the way I'd want it to matter. But I won't go back to the doctor! Not even if I absolutely have to. I take precautions so I'll never have to. All I do is take precautions. That's why I am where I am. But people here know what I'm capable of, they've seen the proof plenty of times.

Though if I misjudge it, and maybe one day I do have to, there'll still be another solution because there's always another solution of some sort, despite my sometimes losing faith in whether the other solution would actually be another solution. But for the time being I'm living how I live. The doctor was so confident at her desk: "You just have to have faith! In this world given to us by God, the Savior has shown every one of us the path; by His example every one of us can choose our own version of salvation. Yes, have faith and everything will change for you." Maybe she said: *Around you*, and I think instead of *change* she used another word. And then she said if I did finally make my mind up and I made the right decision, with that decision I'd soon receive answers to my questions, if I still had any questions following my decision, because she thought I wouldn't, and she also said the love would lift me up and fix everything I'd thought was past fixing, I just had to wait and see. Then, as far as I can remember, she wrote out the prescriptions, stamped them, and repeated what I had to do to be mentally and physically stable again. This was in the Psychiatric Surgery of the new hospital a few days after I arrived back from Versoix, or, to be more precise, exactly two and a half months before I was taken to casualty.

In the building, no one paid any notice of the grill. Or more precisely the artist was the only one to bring it up one time we met. She said, "Here, tell us, for the love of god, what's the point in sticking up that ugly thing?! Do you not see even my flat's in no danger?" I don't remember what I answered, and the other residents never talked about my floor, where essentially it's just me. The artist lives on the half-floor with her husband. Beside their flat was a niche in the wall, and when it wasn't full of their things, it could be used as a hiding place. Their flat was the one directly below the old lady's, which sometimes led to mutual problems for various reasons; exactly why, I don't know, I can't trust the old lady. When something comes to a head, sometimes Heddi beats the bathroom tiles or something else with a broom, and sometimes the artist yells up through the air vent, go on, shove your pissing shit around, why don't you, who do you think you are, the gods in heaven?! There are times when they resolve differences by other means, which also lead to arguments, but at least then they take a bit more care in selecting their words.

How can you separate what you are from what you're not, I've no way of judging, like I'd come home to my own dead body; moreover, this statement isn't true to you until it happens; I guess that's the same kind of thing as what I was thinking before, I seem unable to be precise and to make sense, especially when this whole thing comes over me as if it was stuck to me, a tangle of glittering strands that couldn't possibly feel hot or warm, but it does; and then there's a coldness and a sort of rumbling, dots; you have to be careful not to let it take control, you have to come up with something that instant, anything, just don't allow what wants to stay to stay, you're the one who has to want it, sometimes repetition helps, the same thing ten times in a row, a hundred, a thousand, more if needs be, perhaps while moving, moving a single body part is enough, whatever works.

It's not hard for me to work out certain residents' opinions of me. For some time now I haven't even had to look at their faces, I can read it in their bearing. I do have late payments and I do have debts. That's a fact. There may be other objections. That, too, is a fact. But considering our relationship, I still find the attitude excessive. Sometimes I catch them staring. They watch me like I'd no idea who I was or where I came from. Budapest people have a flair for this. Once, Viola Galambosné seemed to be saying the same, just differently put: "Hungarians are so full of themselves. They need to take a look in the mirror and see who they really are; they stick their noses in the air, while everything around them is slop. Take a look around, son!"

Every time, it's always the same, even in spite of what's different it's the sameness that defines it, and yet, you can't claim the whole thing might not come over you any differently, as you'd explained to that doctor. We were in the surgery. I don't know whether she understood or not, or whether I was understandable or not, because most of the time not even I can grasp in what form what's playing out is playing out. If I could I'd be able to tell her a lot more. There are breaks, maybe that much I can say. For example, I can remember far back enough to know that last time it began with joy. I was walking into a building from somewhere and I was happy I was where I was, I thought maybe this would last longer, I'd every reason to think so, when a young couple appeared beside me; I started hurrying ahead because I didn't want to be near them, I didn't want to hear the language; which language isn't important, I didn't want to hear a certain language. And I arrived at a waiting room where I had to stop to give my name, same as the others. After a while a tall woman came who directed us into a corridor, I mean, another corridor rather than the previous corridor, and there were people there too. We were waiting to be admitted somewhere. That's when the tall woman came over and she said I would go on my own to yet another corridor. That could be when it began. I think so because after some time, the woman was standing beside me again and saying she hadn't told me to go where I was now, she'd told me to go where she'd pointed to, which was distressing; I suddenly understood it seemed I wasn't even capable of completing the simplest of tasks. Meanwhile, I remembered the ticket; not by chance, as I'd seen one of the men standing beside me holding his two minutes before. I immediately started searching for my own; I couldn't find it. That's when I felt it had started again. Or rather at this moment, for the first time it occurred to me it was coming. And it did, even though not long before I had thought I'd reached a point where it'd be a while before it happened again; it lasted a split second but I knew I knew it was coming, and I knew what was coming would feel whichever way it was going to feel, and later, sure enough, that's exactly how it felt because I'd known exactly how it was going to feel; and it did feel like that, but I could only feel it, no matter how much I struggled to grasp what was happening to me, I no longer understood it, because what I knew was coming came, it really came, then I concluded this time that was how it'd begun; meanwhile, I was dripping with sweat and the tall woman had noticed. I'm saying all of this afterward, it's afterward I think it, like so many other things whose cause I'm still to understand.

Maybe it wasn't in the doctor's office I brought it up but somewhere else. Somewhere you can talk about these things, or these things are talked about, but if I was explaining it I must have been at the doctor's.

I don't know. Sometimes I mix up where and what I'm saying, if I'm even the one saying it, because sometimes it feels like it isn't me, it's the other. Me and the other. Unless I always was the other. A kind of being me, where I'm not the one that's me?! Another being-me being being me, or being the as-I'm-saying-this-me? I'm saying this and this isn't what I'm saying. I often think this and this isn't what I often think. If it were any different, clearly my situation wouldn't be the way it is. There wouldn't be any confusion inside me; I could finally make a distinction, I could separate the me from the part inside me not-me, and actually sometimes I can. If I could just stop forgetting what I am! A kind of being, where the inaccessible part of you is you, what's most essentially you! Constantly feeling what you are isn't you but someone else, while afterward, bit by bit you understand it wasn't your own decision, what just happened happened the way it happened, if what happened even happened at all. Besides, saying still isn't knowing. The most comfortable would be thinking, if the thought had the feel of being from this side of the other, or if that's not possible, the feel of being from the far side of the other. When and to which I could say: I'm this. When I could declare finally: I'm this, and this.

I haven't had any guests for years. It wasn't always like this. The Galambos know, they have a perfect view into my flat; at one point they could roughly gauge how I led my life. "You've a fair amount of skirt at your doorstep! We always said you're a rake!" they'd say. Even so, I was never considered to be a social person. Anyone who's ever known me knows what that means, even though I've partially tried to hide my reasons over the years, and successfully, I think; I wouldn't say there's any point in speaking about it; anyway, it's more effective if we don't discover any more than is necessary about ourselves.

I don't remember when and how this period began. Or I do know, it's just pointless talking about it, maybe I wouldn't even be able to. It's enough to know I was left by someone. It doesn't matter by whom or when, or under what circumstances; the point is it happened because of a younger man. I think the person involved was right, in their position I would have done it even earlier. I admit from that point on I became somewhat more cautious, and without a doubt I began treating things very differently. I suppose this could have contributed to my isolation. It's not as though sooner or later we don't naturally become experts at shaking others off anyway. Barely a few months pass, a couple of years, and suddenly it's not just specific people you're playing hide-and-seek with, but essentially everyone you've ever been in touch with.

In the meantime, I carried on doing the same things as I'd done before, except I did them alone, unable to tell what had changed and how. If it had at all. It's often nearly impossible to notice fundamental changes happening inside us; we might not even want to. Then all of a sudden you realize everything is moving of its own volition without your having to invent more tricks; you grow distant, more and more distant, until you gradually get to a point where you can't speak about why and how a new direction came about in your life, if there is such a thing in such matters as a direction or directions.

But I don't mind that this is what happened. On the contrary, I'd feel cheated if everything had stayed as it was. You can live among others in different ways, I experience it every day. I'm coming to realize certain things aren't far from my own nature at all. You can look at what's happening in the world from without. Lona has a lot to say on that. I often avert my gaze as she sits in her wheelchair listening to Mrs. Scheiber; Mrs. Scheiber is Lona's next-door neighbor. I visited her on some matter once. I've been in quite a number of places. At one time perhaps too many, although things were different for me then and not just financially. That's changed since then. Now I watch almost everyone from a distance, which was always typical of me but admittedly not as much as now. This is definitely a development of the last years.

Never having visitors has its advantages. For example, you don't have to explain yourself so much. People asking questions on the street is enough—where am I now, am I really where I am or am I somewhere else, have I left those places I was, where people were talking all sorts about me, or have I not, did I really leave that other one, like some had been spreading about the town for a while now, or did I not leave that other one contrary to reports, which wouldn't have surprised them, the opposite would have surprised them, and these days am I still doing what I was doing for years, or have I stopped doing what I was doing for years, which would honestly be surprising and not surprising at all; and so on, about work, about travel, about relationships—that's all people are interested in.

Though I feel I did have visitors one time. The famous actor's nephew had popped up and he didn't make any insinuations about hospital rooms. That was when one or two of my former students still knew me, either around August sometime or a bit later. We ran into one another by chance near the Opera, not far from where I kept meeting the man with the matted hair selling magazines. I was coming from the Belcantó, where I'd just been told I was too late for the position, he was maybe coming from one of the nearby cafés. I've no idea why I invited him up, which still amazes me because at that time, I didn't let anyone into my flat. It's difficult to speak about the whole thing, because that's when I got the phone call from Germany, and it was during those days I'd been in casualty, and there was something else—I don't remember the rest. One or two things at most. But I couldn't draw the more detailed outlines. I wouldn't gain much by copying in here the order in which I quit my teaching positions, and how I was doing around that time. I taught in a number of art schools in Budapest and for a while I taught at ELTE university, not literature, something else. I worked hard to practice this profession. For a long time, people around me didn't believe I could graduate, which they were right to think, after all, at H… Agricultural Complex, as far as I know, no one ever graduated. I managed to, and for a long while it really seemed as if I'd climbed my way to the top; for years I was able to do what from behind the bars of my cage I'd once thought unattainable, and which I still could be doing if one day I hadn't got into my businesses abroad, the consequences of which I hadn't counted on either at the beginning of my travels or during later events.

Maybe he hasn't noticed anything about me, I must have thought, and that was why I let him up; if in a situation you think someone doesn't think what you think about yourself, or at least if you imagine they can't think what you believe they most likely think of your thoughts, rather than not think of your thoughts, because somehow that's what the signs show, then it's immediately easier to think of yourself not thinking about the other person everything you would usually think almost instantly, or if not think, then suppose, which is immediately a different and more constructive thought, depending on whether you consider your supposition to be part of your own thinking or not part of it, of course while considering, whether you even deem it possible or not to think of all this as being your own, or as someone else's, or maybe as something else's, and whether with that, at the same time, you won't unintentionally think it and not think it, moving thought as thought into a field beyond and below thought, if that's possible when you're sane, because if it is, the whole thing starts over, and if it isn't, the whole thing still starts over or starts somewhere else.

He started talking to me in front of the Yeshiva; for some reason I imagined he was looking at me like his teacher, who of course wasn't his teacher anymore, and in fact wasn't even a teacher anymore, but probably at some point said this and that to him about a poet or a movement, at the Secondary School of Visual Arts where for years I taught literature among other things; at one time, I led a drama group which I'd set up myself. On National Day, with this student of mine playing the lead role we put on a play by a Hungarian poet, which begins: I touched you. You touched me. The show can begin. The work is called *Tableaux* and it's about the war or our ability to depend on air. When my old student entered the flat all he said was: "Christ, sir, nobody's cleaned around here for a while!" Yes, I said, and I gave him the book or whatever it might have been, because he must have come up for some sort of book or something of the kind; and then he left.

After that visit, I reflected on a few things. I knew I had to do something, of course I did, after all, I knew very well about the bottles, how could I not know about the wine bottles, the beer bottles and the other bottles, because they were all over the flat and in front of the flat, in the kitchen and in the toilet, because I squeezed them in between the toilet bowl and the small bath, as many as possible, at the same time, I often filled the bath, not to mention the bookshelves where I could hardly find a thing; the room from floor to ceiling looked like a storehouse. From week to week and month to month I avoided what was gathering in the flat, I crammed them wherever I could, from the bed to the table, from one shelf to the other corner, I kicked them as I traveled down corridors of glass from the bedroom to the kitchen, and so on and so forth. I knew that at forty years old I was supposed to be doing all of this differently, and I knew that all of this wasn't pointless in the way I thought, and the similarities and the nonsimilarities, but if I couldn't, then I couldn't. If you can't pick up the glass bottle, you can't pick it up, you can't, and that's that. If you're not able, you're not able, and that's that; it doesn't work, for some reason it doesn't work; you're simply unable to bend over, for some reason you're simply unable to bend over, and you can't make the decision, either this way or that, to gather up a few and to bring them downstairs.

Last time, the doctor didn't even ask how much my daily dosage was, after the usual she always started with the checkup, the tests, hands out in front and all the rest; I could hardly stand up straight, I was swaying and my hands were still shaking; or by then maybe not so much. Standing with my arms outstretched it seemed as though they were shaking less than in the beginning, when she said, relax your hands please, don't clench them. At least that's something, I thought. During the latest test, she gave the same familiar command, she didn't leave it out, though there was no need to say it, she could see my fingers, my hands; I don't know how long I'd been stuffing them in my pockets in all sorts of situations, when I was paying, when I was showing my ticket, when I was showing my ID, when I was in the chemist's, right when I had to use them.

I usually kept them in my pockets or I tried to distract myself in some other way. It's best if you grip something hard, and if you don't have something, you have to press at the back of your hand. Once, I had to come off my route so I could do my business in the Burger King on Váci Street. When I went down the stairs and I saw the woman behind the desk, I was amazed. I used to come here regularly, but there was never any charge or supervision, it seemed the manager had become aware of people like me. Somehow I gathered together the fifty forints, while the woman stared at my hands; the expression on her face was something like: *It's ones like this who shit all over the seats.* I think she'd have happily escorted me into the stall to oversee my urination.

Once, at the corner shop thieves' I had to hold one hand down with the other, pressing my elbows into my sides hadn't helped, the tremor hadn't gone away. That day, I went in because of the old lady who'd secretly been getting me to buy her brandy, because she'd promised Lona she wouldn't drink any more spirits because of her lungs. She insists on a particular brand, which I could only buy there. The short blond was at the cashier's, the only one it was possible to like; when she's at the till, after a moment's delay sometimes, I hear her greet me, not like in most shops, where you go in and you say hello, and nothing. Somehow I paid, while thinking to myself, these people had to watch all of this. And then I stopped caring; let them think there are days I've broken down altogether.

The last time it was taking its course, I mostly went to the shopping malls. To Westend and Corvin. I thought in these places *it* wouldn't happen, which doesn't even happen, it's just there, all of a sudden it's there, because it doesn't happen, it'll just be there, all of a sudden without any warning it'll be there, regardless of the fact you're trying, you're only ever trying for it not to be; and I thought among other people I wouldn't know, but it isn't knowing, all of a sudden it's just here, you feel it, you don't dare to lie down, you just stand, you don't dare to sit, you stand, you stand on the spot, maybe so you can just sway on the spot, you can't do anything else, you think you can't; and then you have to walk, you walk, you walk, you just walk, later you stand again, you just stand, you don't sit down, you can't sit down. One time I did sit. In Frici Papa's eatery. Back then I could still go into a place like that; I ordered some kind of meat with rice, after I don't know how long I noticed the gypsy man—he was sitting opposite me at the same table; we were both sitting in the corner, he was eating, I wasn't, I remember I didn't even touch the food, I just waited for the whole thing to pass, but it didn't, that's right, it didn't even change, nothing changed at all, it didn't even waver, nothing wavered, which is often worse than if the whole thing got stronger; then at some point he said: "I like you, pal, I like you, but you need to take care of yourself!" That was in my head as I left the restaurant, nothing else, afterward the whole day it was the only thing I could think about, that sentence, which isn't a sentence, because a sentence is different, a sentence is a sentence, I repeated it, a sentence is a sentence, I was walking, just walking, the same as before, except this time I avoided all the sections I didn't usually avoid, the Academy of Sciences, the bridges, one or two tram stops and the rest, tired, I have to be tired, to tire myself out, that's the only way, on Margit Island, in the park, that's what I did in those days, when the whole thing was on top of me, because it was more on top of me than in me; I was running in the part next to the zoo, around the flower beds, on the inside path, where the snow melts less, between stumps, as far as I remember I was wearing running shoes, but I didn't mind the puddles, I just counted the laps, around and around, as I run I can hear the breath, my breath, it must be my breath, he thinks, so I'm the one running, because I'm the one who can feel the water on my socks, the gravel under my toes, I can feel the cold, he feels, or I must be the one who can feel it, the sand doesn't stick, or won't hang together, there's sand everywhere but it won't stick, bits will, but more often it won't.

ERIC BURGER
Mystery Music

I liked the joyful sound of the piano coming from the open door where a few departing partygoers giggled, arms linked. I went in. But despite the pianist's spirit and those lively partygoers, this party was on its last legs. A brown-haired woman with a brass hoop around her neck and an empty martini glass in her hand was sleeping, curled in an armchair. A pudgy man in a silver shirt, looking both pleased with and done with his party effort, tucked in his shirt and said to his friend, "I just can't help but leave a bit of myself everywhere I go." Then they left. None of him lingered in the air. There was just a winding down down down feeling and the now-quieter piano music filling the big, uncarpeted space. I walked over to the hoop woman to check out her grip on the martini glass. The piano playing suddenly got icy and jagged, like some brutal directive. It was telling me *something*. But what was I supposed to do, whip out a kitchen knife and stab her for crying out loud? Have a psychotic break? The piano must have been in the back room, but it felt like it was on top of me, inside me. Then the playing switched to wooly and sad, like the feeling that might accompany remembrance of a keen-eyed tenth-grade girlfriend who first drifted away—you saw her sometimes in the hallways—and then moved to Argentina. But what to do with this? This was a bossy, yet vague piano. I sat down in the empty arm chair next to the hoop woman, who still slept with the martini glass clutched in her fist like a rattle. The piano playing got quieter, sweeter. I closed my eyes. A sunlit commuter train clattered into my head bearing characters from my childhood that I hadn't thought about in decades: an elderly customer on my paper route who had a parakeet named Clyde, a massively mustachioed hotdog vendor whom I found curious once at a basketball game, a quiet girl from art class who threw crayons at the window. The train slowed down down down while I remembered, while people lost from my life came back to me. A strange mercy from the universe, which tries to help us in ways clumsy and divine.

GRADY CHAMBERS
The Plows

By then, simple questions
had grown blades: *you're not even going to shave*

came to mean,
I don't like the way you look,

or that's how I came to hear it.
On certain days she'd say, *do you love me today?*

and I would say, *even more than yesterday,*
and she'd say, *that's impossible!*

and I'd say, *it's true,* and would forget,
as I convinced her, sitting near her in the booth,

the nights spent fuming
mutely through our rooms,

hardly saying anything, the groan of pipes
tightening inside the walls, following each other silently to sleep

until in the night we startled awake
from the sound the plows made

dropping their heavy lower lips
against the pavement, and she'd rise, and I'd follow,

and from the window watch
the wet red brake lights disappearing

at the turn, and the new plowed streets shining
black as snakes

amidst the piled snow.

JIM DANIELS
Highlights of the Low Lights

She held my dog's paw like a gentle jewel.
Wind blew her hair into a moonlit arc of ocean.
I sat on the tub while she shaved her legs.
We shrugged in the downpour.

Playground wings and swings, unchained laughter.
The pop of her lips released the bottle and her grin.
Naked on the porch.
Abandoning the stalled car forever.

Pancakes, syrup, indecent proposal.
Fish dart through dawn's quiet lake.
A variety of ridiculous hats.
The discovery of raspberries.

My letter, her envelope.
Map rising into a kite.

DARYL FARMER
Once a River

"It is the only way to end poverty," says El Presidente. I look at the land below us and yearn for green and blue, instead of this ash gray, dust brown. A hazy sun. My eyes burn. I have not been home for going on two hundred days. This morning, I looked in the mirror and saw my liquid eye squinting out from leathered skin. A murmuring babble coming from my lips, something about another source-become-friend now dead. People associate my name with violence, think I must like it, all the horrific acts, but I don't. I confess to be drawn to it, absorbed by it, obsessed with the way it manifests itself in the most unlikely ways. But when I left the camp, and returned to the hotel amid the ruins, I wept. There's predator and prey, which is just survival, and then there's sport, the doing that comes simply from the knowing that you can. Then there's a kind of power that's the last step before evil. Or maybe evil comes first.

It seems odd to me that El Presidente is piloting this helicopter, but he likes to fly, he says, has learned to trust only what he himself controls. Information deemed classified—yet passed on to me, thereby declassifying it—shows at least seventeen assassination attempts on El Presidente. I asked him yesterday if this was true, and he seemed offended.

"Surely," he said, "there have been more."

I have known El Presidente for over twenty years. Our first interview was in a small hotel room, two chairs, no bed. Why? I asked him. He shrugged, said he didn't need one, had given up sleep. It was his custom, he said, to have all furniture removed wherever he stayed. He liked to pace, and if he did need to sit, he rested against a wall. The chairs in that room were a courtesy, on my account. He seemed to me then a mystic, and against my own cynicism, I found him charming, despite that charred lithified face so badly burned it reminded me of wax once dripping now hardened. I couldn't take my eyes off him. He wore wire frame specks then, the lenses magnified, so as to bring to mind a giant fly. I asked him if he'd ever considered surgery.

He smiled. "And why?" he asked. "To mask all that I have survived? No, friend. My face is my history."

This was before the coup that had brought him to power, before the dark black glasses that would become his trademark. Too small for his face, these glasses. Now he looks not like a fly but a bespectacled snake.

I am sitting in the copilot's seat. Earlier, he had offered us each a blindfold. When I refused, he'd smiled, shrugged. There are five of us. The woman sitting behind me is the wife of a commander whose name you used to see on the news, that same commander who now sits in a federal prison for a betrayal against immorality. Crime of all crimes, he told the truth, finally. Sometimes treason is just a man with a conscience, though he found his a little too late. Last night, I saw her, the wife, sitting alone in a corner of the hotel bar. I noticed she was crying. That is to say, tears streamed down her face, but she stared straight ahead with that distant look that I had heretofore only seen in soldiers, victims. Now that look is everywhere. A longing for a home that would never again exist for her. I walked to the table, meant to offer her some kindness, not knowing what that might even be. "Fuck off," she'd said, without looking at me. I had left her to her horrors. Today, when offered the blindfold, she had taken it without a word. She wears it now, though we are many miles from the refugee camp. The people who end there will have walked over a hundred starving miles. It is estimated that only about 37 percent of those who begin that journey will survive.

The other two people here, I don't know who they are. They seem like a couple, but I think that only because I saw them sitting across from each other not talking in the hotel lobby before we left. She is one of those gracefully aging women, worldly and unfazed. At their best when sweating with their hair pulled back. They are to trouble as El Presidente is to death; they court it and then remain unfazed. Can stand in the middle of a killing field and analyze as if it's all just an ancient text. When I looked at her earlier, she smiled at me as if we were in collusion. We are not. I didn't smile back.

The man she either is or is not with wears shades, has a perfect tan. He reeks of security, a body guard for El Presidente, I presume. Except, he has a mouth full of grotesque teeth—crooked, brown-stained. Horrendous. This man's teeth make no sense to me. Of the security men I have known in my life—and I have known many of them—they have all had perfect teeth.

El Presidente is only partially responsible for the heartbreak that is passing for progress here. He has risen to his place by selling what they all do. You think oil, petroleum, pharmaceuticals. No. That is economy. This is power. Power relies on a different kind of commodity: fear and hope. Control perception of these two things, and you control the world. El Presidente has convinced his allies, including my own government (though publicly they are enemies), that the refugees are to be feared, and he is their lone hope against this fear. Publicly, they denounce him. Meanwhile, and miraculously, his wealth grows and grows, his military has an ever increasing supply of munitions. Before that commander discovered his conscience, I had asked him about this, despite warnings the question was off-limits. He pretended to know nothing. I have been watched closely since. Men in suits and dark glasses follow me. My landline phone was tapped, until I yanked its cord from my wall for good.

A month before I arrived here, I was invited by a woman who should have known better to a dinner party in a capital city. I was told it was formal. I wore jeans and a bolo tie.

"Oh," she'd said when I met her in the lobby "Didn't I tell you to dress up?"

"Yes," I said. "And I did."

She gave me one of those exasperated looks I've grown accustomed to. I half hoped she would say "just forget it" and move on without me.

But instead, she smiled. "Let's go, then," she said.

It was one of those parties important people throw. I've been to a handful of them, and every time, I promise myself never again. I liked this woman, knew the night would end with us together in one of our hotel rooms rutting like carnivores until spent. Then we'd lie, isolates in our own respective silences as we stared at the ceiling in the dark. The sex would be fine, but it was that moment of sadness after that I'd crave really. I realize how damaged I've become.

The moment we arrived, I knew it was a mistake. Ceiling chandeliers that left that peach light around everyone. People in suits and gowns. Underlings looking to get close to the powerful. Everybody smiling, happy, charming. Imported wine, of course. Food to feed a nation, most of which would be thrown away at the end. It all made me dizzy.

She looked at me. "Try to enjoy it," she said.

I heard myself growl. A tray with glasses of champagne passed, and against my better instincts, I grabbed one. Then later, two more. Suddenly, I didn't like the looks I was getting. I saw a man I didn't recognize lean down to whisper in her ear. They both looked at me. She shrugged. But she never pretended to not be there with me. My presence was a considerable risk to her career. Also, she was using me to make a point. Fine. It was a point we shared. I'm not ashamed of what happened next.

A senator who'd recently penned and promoted a policy masked as "economic growth" but would clearly—should anyone care to sift through the fine print—serve to further empower El Presidente and result in the chaos erupting before us now, made a point of approaching the woman I was with just as a camera miraculously appeared. It was an image that would position him well in his home state, which also happened to be hers. Proof of a willingness to work together. Proof that he didn't *actually* hate women. My guess was that her poll approval had recently risen, their demographics had intersected. In all wars of the future, I suggest champagne as our only weapon. In any case, it was what I had, so I flicked the drink in his face just as the camera flashed. It struck me the perfect image, but of course never made the news.

He was enraged, but he didn't square up. Men like him never do. He looked immediately for his security, two men who had already grabbed me.

"You're way out of your league here, Pal," he said.

Pal, Sport, Buddy, Chief. These are names I will not cop to.

"Murderer," I hissed. Then I took the glass from her hand and splashed him again.

He wiped his face with his hand. "Goodbye," he said, and his goons—perfect straight and very white teeth, every one of them—led me away.

"Murderer!" I hollered again, and I kept yelling it as they dragged me out of the hotel.

When she found me, nearly an hour later, I was sitting at the far end of the bar two blocks over, nursing the cheapest glass of red wine I could find. I like cheap. Cheap does less damage in the world. I was surprised to see her. I give her credit.

"Well, you shouldn't have done that," she said.

Should. Shouldn't. There must be a way for shoulds to override shouldn'ts. That party had been so full of shouldn'ts, my shouldn't shouldn't have even registered. Shoulds died long ago, with mushroom clouds in the desert, wiretapping, covert arms operations to fund evil dictators. Probably before then. I have no shoulds left to give. I started this career, or penance, or whatever the hell it is, a million years ago because I thought people should know, thought that the truths I told would shed a light so bright on the world that should would be all we had left. But shouldn'ts reign, and reign and reign and shoulds are more and more buried in the acid yellow dust left behind.

"Of course, I should have," I said.

She sighed. "What are we drinking?" And she settled into the seat beside me.

"Kool-Aid, apparently," I said.

"God, do you even own a tie?" she asked.

I do not.

Our later coupling was loud and shook the fancy hotel walls. I hoped the Senator was in the next room over to hear us. The ensuing sadness carried me forward for days. In the morning, I boarded the first of six flights, the last of which brought me here.

I look back now at Teeth Rot. He is staring at me, not smiling. The land below is surprising to me. Scrub brush, and gnarled trees that remind me of some mix of bristlecone and Joshua trees. It used to be the first thing I would do before traveling to a new place, learn the names of the trees. It's the first step to knowing a place. When had I stopped doing that? It suddenly became very important that I know the names. I turned to El Presidente.

"What are these trees?" I asked, gesturing.

He looked at me, bemused. "Perhaps I seem to you a tourist guide?" He laughed. I wondered if he knew how much I hated him. I looked back at Teeth Rot. He shook his head, turned to look out his window.

It is to my advantage, I suppose, that mainstream masses don't know me; not by name, not by sight. I am a dying-breed journalist. Not a household name, but I sell enough books to keep me fed and alert. *Cult* is the word they use to describe my following. I was on CNN once. The woman asked me a question. I answered it honestly, a truth that did not jibe with the network correspondent's earlier report. I was never asked back. It's not that I'm not willing to play the game; it's just that no one ever gives me the rulebook. It seems to me the key is to feign a knowledge you don't really have. I have my eyes, my ears. I know a world that doesn't fit well into clips that weave around commercials. But I've only been doing this for thirty-three years. I play witness. I file reports that few people read. I watch the reports seen by millions instead. I scratch my head. It's enough to make the sanest of men drink.

What is about to happen here, I will report. A handful of people will read it. It won't matter. If my report does get attention—any attention at all—I will be called names by those whose power is Teflon-cloaked. By those who have mastered the art of seducing a camera. By those who will hide behind masks of anonymity, and whose darts will be venomous as snakes and relentless. They will call me a liar, and I will, by then, be sitting on my desert porch drinking red wine, a rattler—an actual snake, a rare breed, being of the trustworthy kind—resting at the foot of the porch stairs. At that point, even I will question what I've seen. I long for the therapist who can convince me it's all been hallucination.

Just a week before, after negotiating the opportunity through channels that included El Presidente's publicity office, agencies in my own government, and the humanitarian group currently permitted to organize supply and food drops, I walked among the refugees. The day was surprisingly cold, and I wish I'd thought to bring a jacket. Children—war-torn, also known as life-torn, because life and war were one and the same here, their lips like chipped bark, their skeletons visible behind translucent skin—surrounded me. They sang a song I can only describe as exultation. That song will haunt me until the day I die. I rarely take photos anymore. Cameras make the people I generally talk to nervous. I don't use voice recorders either. I listen. I watch hands. Nothing betrays emotions like human hands. Hands reveal truth and hands reveal lies. I always prepare questions, but rarely refer to them. Hands more than anything guide my interviews. But this time, I took photos of the children, wished I'd recorded their singing. My camera has since been confiscated. It doesn't matter, probably. *If only the world knew* is not a phrase I use anymore. The world knows and shrugs. I could have posted those photos, and there would have been five seconds of outrage before disappearing behind some athlete or congressman's latest escapades.

There was a boy among the children. In one eye he was blind, pure white like an egg, but his good eye met mine and held me there, challenged me with his song, which seemed to rise above the others. I had a packet of peanut butter crackers in my pocket, and I took one and gave it to him, though I'd been told to bring no food. "Don't feed the refugees," the aid worker from the humanitarian organization had told me, as if we were talking about national park bears. "Don't be stupid," I said. But I shouldn't criticize him. Few in this mess mean well, but I am sure he did. Never taking his eyes off me, the boy took the cracker and handed it to a girl beside him, his sister, I presumed. I expected her to devour it, but she nibbled at it slowly. She broke off a piece about the size of a dime, and handed it back to him.

The boy stopped singing and said something I didn't understand. I smiled, shrugged, indicating my ignorance. So, he grabbed my wrist, pulled, and I let him guide me. He led me past a line of makeshift canopies. People sat in clusters by fires. A woman was shaking a rug. Another stirred a pot over a fire as she held a baby to her breast. They all stopped to watch as we passed. The singing continued, a new song. The boy led me inside a dark tent. It took a moment for my eyes to adjust, and when they did I saw the man. He was sitting on the ground. He wore a black, thread-bare T-shirt. It was hard to make out the logo on the shirt at first, but then I saw that it was for a Canadian beer. His eyes were closed, his hands folded in front of him. His thumbs moved, tapping a rhythm. The tent was warm, and smelled of wood burning. I could still hear the children, their song moving away from us. I sat across from the man.

"Why do they sing, the children?" I asked.

"For you."

He spoke with a heavy accent, but in my own language. Because he knew my language, but I did not know his, a fact that shamed me.

"Me?" I asked.

"They have been told you are the teller of stories," he said.

I understood this meant something specific to them, something meaningful. I was not who they hoped me to be. My own culture did not work that way. But I nodded.

The man had still not looked at me.

"And what story should I tell?" I asked.

The man sat in silence for several moments, thinking. His stillness unnerved me.

"Once," said the man, "there was a woman, and there was rain. Then there was a river. And the river was the rain's gift to the woman. Take care of the river, said the rain, and I will always fill it for you. The woman had a daughter, and they lived by the river, taking sustenance from it, giving praise to it. This is the first story. The girl grew to be a woman. This woman is my mother who has died. Now there is no rain. We are told the river belongs only to those on the other side of a line. But I have journeyed where they say sits this line. There is no line. I look." The man placed his hand across his brow and moved his head from side to side. "No line." The boy crouched beside me. He gazed with wonder upon the man.

"Our young men, many of them, have joined the rebellion, what El Presidente calls the Destroyers. But we are not what is said of us, either way. Not bringers of death. Not warriors. No. We are farmers. But what is there to farm?" He unfolds his hands, spreads them across the room, gesturing. "Rage replaces crops. And so our men, hungry, feed their rage with acts of vengeance."

I watched the man's hands as he spoke. They were long, slender. The veins created a topography that reminded me of the alluvial fans near the desert where I live. Two years ago, twenty-seven men died in that desert. They had crossed a similar invisible line. The story was told in a book. That book was banned in the state where I live. Stories run like rivers. They, too, must be filled.

"I have four sons," said the man. "Do you understand? It is not about approval, or shame. It is about understanding." For the first time, he looked at me. "Do I have four sons? Or did I? I do not know the answer to this question.

"El Presidente, he calls us leeches. But how can that be? Leeches live only where there is water. You see, he has taken our water from us. In our story, it is told, be wary of one who hides his eyes. In our story, a devil with black eyes steals the river from us. This story is very, very old.

"We have suffered through a long journey. Many of us died. This, too, is an old story, told again and again. Children, women. The elders were most important to me. I tried to learn their stories before they died, but many stories died with them.

"You tell this, now. We are not guerillas, or killers. We live in a story. It is the only way we know how to live. Our story is broken. I am not the right one to tell it. But I am the only one."

The man said something to the boy in the language I didn't understand, and the boy rose, returned with two small clay cups, handed me one. Inside, there was a tablespoon worth of liquid. The man and I both drank from the cups. The tea tasted like the earth; from the mug it was like drinking from a stream.

The man looked at me. "When you tell this story," said the man, "tell them you heard it from a ghost."

Now, I see the camp in the distance, ragged tents in the dust. El Presidente is looking at me. I wonder if he is thinking about that first interview, my dangerously challenging questions, his soft-spoken, intelligent, and surprisingly honest answers. Why me? He rarely talks to any press, even in his own country where he himself controls their words. I'm trying to expose him as an evil to be dealt with, but the masses, the unaffected masses, are intrigued by him. Hate him as you will, he sells advertising. He looks at me now, but I just stare straight ahead. In the reflection, I can see the commander's wife. I want to turn to her, rip the blindfold from her face. Traumatized as she already is, why should she, too, not be haunted by this?

What is about to happen, I could try to stop. Later, when this account is published, should you happen to read it, you can justifiably believe that I should have, yes. At least that I should have tried. I could take the controls from El Presidente, guide us to a fiery crash, my own fitting end with the rest of them. But I know Teeth Rot would stop me. Already I can feel his eyes burning the back of my neck in anticipation of any move I make. Life is not an Indiana Jones movie. The good guys in fact rarely win. Besides, my story would never be reported. Words, I still believe, are the only true weapon against evil in the world, even though I sometimes fear evil is so far ahead, and the world's words have betrayed us all.

My father wanted me to be a doctor; the irony is that I did not believe I could stomach the blood. My mother wanted me to be a priest. I chose journalism instead. I have spent much of my reporter's life in the dark shadows of the world, have delved into its despair it is true;

but even in that despair I hold hope. Among the many battles I wage is my own fight against cynicism. Cynicism advantages oppressors. I believe in hope, even amid these horrors of today. I want you to know I have seen profound kindness in the world; priests who wash the feet of those who live in dumpsters, poets who sit listening by the bedsides of the dying and wounded. A boy who shares a cracker with his sister, and the sister who breaks off a chunk and passes it back. By following El Presidente to this moment, I have edged ever closer to evil, but in that closeness, I sense its vulnerabilities. Evil relies on a belief of its own inevitability, that it is a force that cannot ever be eradicated. I refuse to believe this. The battle may be larger than the length of my life, but, yes, I hold out hope. I cannot stop El Presidente, not today. Instead, I can only bear witness, can tell you this story.

The refuge is below us now, the copter dips. People are running to us because they associate helicopters with food. They drop to their knees, pleading. I search for the man, the ghost, among them, but do not find him. But I see the one-eyed boy. He is shirtless, his pants in tatters, his legs like axe handles. For the umpteenth time in my career, I sit helpless before an action that will traumatize me, and I want to scream. This sterile craft is sealed so tightly we can barely hear the engine, but I know those children are singing and I want to hear their song. El Presidente pulls a lever. The air below us fills with a yellow cloud, thick as a storm, and the earth below disappears. Sealed though it is, I can smell the putrid fumes. The sickly fog clears slowly as it disperses. We pass, turn, take another sweep. The refugees are covering their faces, are clawing at their skin. Through the yellow fog, at last I see him again, the boy. He is on his knees now, and he reaches upward, his hands stretched to the sky, to us, his eyes closed as if in sacred benediction. The sprayers release again. The yellow dust hides the world, but still I refuse to turn away.

CHELSEA B. DESAUTELS
Why I Think of Jungle Crows

after Peter Harris

A Japanese shrine is lit by ten thousand candles.
One by one, jungle crows carry the candles away

to the fields. The flight does not extinguish
the flame—the wick remains hot. Then, the crows bury

their new light under dry leaves, saving the tallow
in the wax for another day. They'll eat later.

In the hospital, midwives search my womb
for a baby, but there's no heartbeat and no sign

of miscarriage. Still, blood tests show something
somewhere in my body is pregnant. I lullaby

baby where are you. The women are getting nervous.

The worshippers can't find their candles. The fields are on fire.

EMILY HOFFMAN
The Gilt Mirror

In the tradition of aunts and nieces
we were traveling on the continent,
and, as in the tradition, she had no child;
we slept in one room, in one bed.

What of men? I would sit in the hotel window
in Paris, looking at the people on the street below—
they held no interest.

I had graduated high school.
I was approaching a boundary
with the future, which seemed to me
a barren and luminous expanse,
free of the habitual constraints
but free also of figure, shape,
or subdivision.

We drove to the south.
Fields of poppy, fields of lavender.
She ran her hands up the stalks
to get the scent off the blossoms
and then gave me her hand to smell.

She was easy with her hands.
She would touch strangers,
lay her hand familiarly on the forearm
of the grocer when she mistakenly asked
for pepper, instead of for a pear.

We continued south, down to the coast.
The Roman amphitheater at Arles,
Arles of the sunflowers, of the thick yellow application.
We climbed to the highest ring.

The perimeter encircled the arena
but you could look out the other way over the land,
the countryside: lighter squares and darker—

My aunt embraced me.
Her lips were smooth and dry
against my neck.

She seemed to believe
I would have something resembling a normal life,
though her assurances were very general, having rarely
to do with my qualities or what they
in particular might necessitate or elicit.

We returned to our room
with its canopied bed, the ornate bureau,
and gilt mirror.

I made her talk about men.
Made? She was happy to.

She closed her eyes
to give herself more fully
to the task of memory.

I didn't face her; she was stroking my hair.

Framed by gold branches
we regarded each other.
Dark eyes, dark hair.
She touched my cheek.
Thirty years passed between us
like a sleeping kingdom.

I remember looking out the window at the dark
garden, the moonlit garden.
I imagined myself walking through it
full of feeling, as I was,

the wet quality of the moonlight.

But the moonlight was also contained
in the bed, which had the advantage
of being warm.

I slept very soundly.
It now seems a miracle to me
that I ever woke up.

Gun Oil

Soldiers gnawed
the ends of twigs to make brushes. What they sketched
would be used to identify them
when they were returned
to their families for ancestor worship. Gun oil
as paint. The war-dead accrued
on their papers. Roofs broken in with jacketed lead and herbicides, an expanse
of fire. It was the end
of an afternoon in 1970. The sun wrapped
the big spiky leaves in a cloth of gold.
Soldiers tucked sketches into coffins
to get them back to the hometowns of the dead.
My father was too young to die in that war,
and his father was too old.

GRETCHEN E. HENDERSON
Thinking Like a Crosswalk

We use them every day. Across intersections, white stripes stitch together seams of foot traffic. The ubiquitous stripes signal pedestrian paths that network our built environments. Often called "crosswalks," these pedestrian crossings have evolved over the years to curiously accrue animal names like *zebra crossings, panda crossings, pelican crossings, toucan crossings,* and *puffin crossings.* To get to the other side, it's hard not to think of the joke about the chicken.

To get to the other side, safe and sound, isn't as easy as it seems. In recent months, it has been reported that pedestrian deaths in some cities are at a thirty-three–year high. The numbers are up from 2016 (the year I was hit by a car in a crosswalk) when it was estimated that every day one hundred people in the United States died from traffic accidents. Deborah Hersman, former chairman of the National Transportation Safety Board and now president and CEO of the National Safety Council, describes this as the equivalent of two regional jets crashing each day, or fourteen plane crashes each week. "If we had 14 plane crashes a week, our hair would be on fire and no one would set foot on an airplane," Hersman stated. "Why do we accept the fatalities that occur on our roadways?" The National Safety Council estimates that traffic accidents in the US last year killed around forty thousand people. While not all of the fatalities were pedestrians in crosswalks, that statistic doesn't include those who survived with serious injuries (including myself) that greatly increase the numbers: upward of 2.5 million.

There's something unnerving about our seeming comfort with these odds. Statistics can leave us bleary from abstraction, so to estimate another way: we're far less likely to be struck by lightning than hit by a car. The odds of being struck by lightning in your lifetime are one out of 136,111, according to Edward Humes in *Door to Door: The Magnificent, Maddening, Mysterious World of Transportation.* In contrast, the odds of dying in a car crash are one to 112.

Recall the last time you jumped out of the way of a speeding vehicle or witnessed a collision or its aftermath. If you haven't been hit, you probably know someone who has been—a relative or friend of a friend (likely less than two degrees of separation). For a nation hooked on cars, with international conflicts over fuel for gas-guzzling vehicles, we have developed a codependent relationship that makes allowances for these "accidents." The convenience and speed seem to outweigh the risks, as personal transportation choices tend to favor vehicles more powerful than we need, often carrying a single person with underutilized cargo space. "A death every fifteen minutes," concludes Humes, "is part of the price tag for that convenience, size, and speed."

Even as cars get safer, many humans behind the wheel still do not recognize risks associated with speed, alcohol, or distraction from technology. As we welcome the convenience, it's easy to overlook the threat—that is, until you are blindsided by a vehicle that comes from behind you in a crosswalk, hitting your side, flipping your body up its hood and then down on pavement, where your head gashes and bleeds. A human body of 125 pounds (as I am) is no match for a steel machine weighing two tons. If you are lucky enough to not have your spine broken, other injuries may take months or years to heal, leaving an indelible impression on your body and brain.

The risks increase along demographic lines. People sixty-five years or older and people of color are more vulnerable to being killed by cars while walking. This disparity is especially stark in places like North Dakota, where Native Americans account for 5 percent of the population and nearly 38 percent of pedestrian deaths. Inequities manifest in other ways. When fear of the Ebola virus raged in the United States in 2014, two people died from the virus, compared with the estimated twelve thousand people killed by drunk drivers that year. The fear of the virus provoked racial slurs and cries to close national borders, while vehicular fatalities stacked up as unfortunate "accidents." The public outcry toward one and neglect of the other (two compared with twelve thousand!) exposes the underside of this story.

An estimated 94 percent of crashes can be tied to human choice or error. Vehicular fatalities have been called a "preventable epidemic." Even as safety features are added to cars, the public is slow to change its driving behaviors, and people arguably grow more distracted each day behind the wheel. Signals like traffic lights, stop signs, speed bumps, and crosswalks aim to make drivers slower and more responsible. But improvement may lie not only in networking our cities with more pedestrian crossings. It may also lie in thinking differently about our habits and habitats: what might be called building new crosswalks in our brains.

Following Crosswalks

In its earliest usage in 1744, a "crosswalk" referred to the crisscrossing of paths in a garden. Jane Austen wrote in her novel *Pride & Prejudice* (1813): "Leading the way through every walk and cross walk." Pedestrian crossings of stepping stones date back to ancient Pompeii, where ruts between raised stones allowed carts, rainfall, and sewage to pass through pedestrian corridors while walkers stepped above. Crosswalks in the modern sense arose primarily with the rise of urban life in the nineteenth and twentieth centuries. Pedestrians navigated vehicular traffic first in tandem with horses and carriages and, later, cars. While the earliest crossings in the United States and Britain tend to date to the 1930s (using variations of metal studs on roads and poles to the sides), the world's first striped crosswalk wasn't officially installed until 1951 in Slough, England.

Crosswalks can run perpendicular, horizontal, or diagonally across intersections. Some are painted on pavement, while others are raised and double as speed bumps. There are famous crosswalks to which tourists make pilgrimages, like Abbey Road in London, where the Beatles walked into history on their eponymous album cover. Shibuya Crossing in Tokyo is considered a "pedestrian scramble," also referred to as a "Barnes Dance." The more people who inhabit an area, the more need for crosswalks to courier them safely across intersections.

I am always on the lookout for crosswalks, since walking is my main mode of transportation. Fortunate to live within walking distance (forty minutes) of work in Washington, DC, I commute by foot. Before being hit by a car, I often walked hours each day. Walking to work, walking my dog, hiking with my husband or friends. In 2016, while living in Providence for a research fellowship, the day before my departure, I planned a celebratory day to conclude my stay, starting with a walk to my favorite coffee shop. The day was scheduled with events and reunions; my husband was joining me the next day for a weekend rendezvous; I was grateful for the productive months in Rhode Island

and looking forward to returning home to DC. A few blocks from my residence, at the intersection of Angell and Hope Streets, a traffic light signaled to walk. I stepped into the crosswalk. I don't remember being hit by a two-ton car, except an explosion of pain, then a blank, then confusion and pain-beyond-pain and disorientation, lying on the pavement with my head in the lap of a stranger, who told me that I was hit by a car and bleeding badly and not to move because my spine may have broken, and an ambulance was on its way. Then a surreal blur.

For the first few weeks after being hit, I could walk only with a walker in close confines and had difficulty moving, even a slight turn in bed. While I tried to stay stoic, the physical pain was excruciating; at times when my husband tried to help me move, I couldn't help but yelp or moan. Yet I was deeply grateful to be alive and realized that it could have been much worse. The physical injuries brought a learning curve, to be sure, but the concussion (also called TBI, or Traumatic Brain Injury) seemed more difficult. Noises and music could trigger vertigo, migraines, exhaustion, and an inability to process information. I had nine staples removed from my head, bumpy across my scalp under my hair, masking the resulting injuries where my head had bounced: first, off the colliding SUV, and then off the crosswalk pavement. A physical therapist's test revealed the collision had dislodged otoliths, microscopic stones in my inner ear, which affect the body's ability to balance. (The test: When I tried to lie down, my eyes rapidly jutted left and right for over half a minute, unable to focus—surreal to observe, my husband said, as he observed this on repeated occasions, saying the sight reminded him of *The Exorcist*.) "Active rest" was the doctors' repeated orders. They explained that trying to push would actually make things worse and prolong my recovery. I was off electronics for weeks, could manage almost no reading or writing, and had to give up sustained work for months.

Slowly, my activities resumed. When I got off my walker and regained mobility and stability (after vertigo had subsided, and I was no longer a "fall risk"), my physical therapist wanted to be sure that I built up a cardiac rate to increase blood to my brain. Activity helps you recover from concussion. She recommended that I buy a Fitbit to rebuild my walking routine and amp up my stamina and strength. A speech therapist practiced memory tests and other exercises for my brain. She would set a timer and have me categorize items (*What animals would you find in a zoo?*), or see how many related words I could name (*What fruits begin with the letter F?*), or try to play word game apps (*Red Herring* and *7 Words*). Time, rest, walking, swimming, and physical and speech therapies helped to heal my interconnected brain and body, which needed blood to circulate to activate both physical mobility and thought.

Concussions remain largely mysterious and can yield a wide range of symptoms. At times in my own recovery, I searched for a word and found another word that sounded similar (e.g., seeing a "hubcap" on the street and saying "humpback," or knowing that I had a doctor's appointment for my bones, but saying "optometrist" instead of "orthopedist"), or seeing a clock and confusing the hands, not knowing if they read 11:00 or 2:00. There was a strange feeling that my brain knew the answer but could not access the information. Or I might start a sentence and not know how to finish it, dropping off mid-sentence. Like standing on a street corner without seeing a crosswalk. (Which way to go? How to get to the other side?) When my brain tried to think too hard, my head would spin. I would get dizzy, start to answer a question, and not know how to finish it. Oftentimes, the right word seemed within—but just beyond—my grasp, buried deep in the folds of my cerebral squish.

I finished treatment for my injuries almost a year after the hit. Lucky, all things considered. It helped that I had a loving partner who could assist my most intimate needs, schedule and drive me to doctors' appointments, among the many careful attentions that contribute to a good recovery. Also, the same hit can affect bodies differently. When Clark Elliott, a professor of artificial intelligence and cognitive science in Chicago, was slightly rear-ended in his car, he felt fine and declined to go to the hospital, instead leaving to lecture at the university where he taught. Within days he had trouble remembering his name and the meaning of *Friday*, had difficulty reading and walking, and other debilitating symptoms that derailed his brain and his life for a decade.

According to the US Centers for Disease Control and Prevention, a new concussion case occurs in the US every fifteen seconds, amounting to two million new cases per year. Some of these are caused by vehicular accidents, while others result from injuries suffered by football players, war veterans, and those who experience head trauma, with widely varying results. The brain is a living organism, plastic and changeable, alive as we are, at best able to create new neural connections, adjust to injury, and adapt to changes in environment. This is the basis of neuroplasticity, which largely guides the treatment of concussions. As our environment changes, we need to recalibrate our thinking, reevaluate old directions and consider new potential connections. Essentially, we need to chart new cognitive crosswalks. In some ways, as I have been writing this essay on and off over many months, I am laying out new crosswalks for my brain to follow. Connecting this with that. It may even be helpful to make a mental leap: *To think like a crosswalk.*

Thinking Like a Crosswalk

In *A Sand County Almanac*, the conservationist Aldo Leopold famously encouraged readers to "Think like a mountain." His philosophy appreciated the complex interconnection of all parts of an ecosystem. To "think like a mountain" accounts for centuries of time and space, where stones, wolves, pines, and other flora and fauna grow in and out of one another intimately and interdependently. Humans are only one small part of a larger web. Both human and nonhuman species "think," writes anthropologist Eduardo Kohn in *How Forests Think*, as they learn from experiences reflected in their evolution. Beyond "sylvan thinking," Kohn describes the communicative dances of bees or how wings demonstrate a bird's adaptation around air streams over generations, acting as an expression beyond language. Flight becomes a way to think and, as it acts, continues the learning curve of thought. From the perspective of biology and neuroscience, Robert Sapolsky follows a related thread: "Think like a zebra." From this perspective, he explains *Why Zebras Don't Get Ulcers*: essentially, a zebra's physiological response mechanisms have adapted to deal with short-term physical emergencies, in contrast to humans who increasingly don't know how to shut off these mechanisms. "When we sit around and worry about stressful things," he writes, "we turn on the same physiological responses—but they are potentially a disaster when provoked chronically." If these mechanisms stay on, they essentially become reflected through adaptation as a disastrous mode of thought.

A mountain, a forest, and a zebra are animate in different ways— unlike a crosswalk, which is manmade. Regardless, a crosswalk reflects evolving thought and adaptation as humans make analogous connections across our "built" and "wild" landscapes. A crosswalk becomes not only part of a map (with all the limitations of maps, as infamously represented by a Mercator projection) but also a metaphor. Historian Anne Harrington describes how metaphoric choices create new cognitive connections like crosswalks or "crossroads, the traversing of which has implications for the future." As opposed to thinking like a freeway bypass, thinking like a crosswalk anticipates a social-spatial bridge, where different communities might benefit from a corridor of connection.

In many ways "crosswalks" refer to more than white stripes on pavement. *Crosswalk* has become a formal term for intellectual intersections. They refer to appendices that interlink subjects, classifying and cross-referencing metadata around objects by name, origin, material, and other networkable categories. The Getty Research Institute describes a "crosswalk" "for planning purposes" as "an *intellectual mapping*." I once heard a library described as a "crossroads" to connect different subjects, so it's understandable that "crosswalks" have arisen across both physical and metaphysical terrains. These kinds of crosswalks connect a reader to research and suggest potential directions to follow. Just as crosswalks on pavements are meant to signal where a pedestrian might cross, intellectual crosswalks set up a similar path for a cataloger or curator.

We follow literal and figurative crosswalks every day that signal paths for our bodies and brains. Our intellectual maps often are taken for granted as much as white stripes that link corners across intersections. We consider one point among others to connect a line, to make sense of a subject or a situation, to think and navigate time and space—deciding where to cross a seeming border.

Language lies within our histories of crosswalking. Migrations enabled cultural exchanges, networking thought and communication systems, developing our brains and language. In *Wanderlust: A History of Walking*, Rebecca Solnit describes this phenomenon in urban history. "A city is a language, a repository of possibilities, and walking is the act of speaking that language, of selecting from those possibilities," she writes; "architecture limits where one can walk, but the walker invents other ways to go," including by "crossing." Jean Christophe Bailly correlated language with pedestrianism and called "walking" the "generative grammar of the legs." If the built environment discourages walking, there are cognitive implications, even without concussion from a crash. As Solnit conjectures: "if the city is a language spoken by walkers, then a postpedestrian city not only has fallen silent but risks becoming a dead language, one whose colloquial phrases, jokes, and curses will vanish, even if its formal grammar survives."

Compared with when you drive, walking brings a heightened sense of interaction. There is close proximity, even indirect intimacy, with strangers. A passing glance, a brush against an arm, a smile or wave or grimace. Sights, sounds, smells. Crosswalks are laid out to help pedestrians safely traverse a city; otherwise, walkers would stand stranded on street corners or jaywalk and dodge vehicular traffic. Intersections bring people together in ways that are impossible with freeways, where cars literally bypass, going around or above communities, pushing the speed limit, if not stuck bumper to bumper.

That isn't meant to lump all drivers against pedestrians. Some drivers navigate with utmost care, while some walkers step into oncoming traffic as if expecting the sea to part. Many people combine both modes of transport. The networks that we travel—drivers, walkers, bikers, more—track where we cohabit and, in turn, shape cognition. Neuroscientist Eleanor Maguire has spent almost two decades studying London taxi drivers and discovered the enlargement of the posterior hippocampus: the area of the brain considered most important for memory. London cabbies have to pass what has been called "the hardest test, of any kind, in the world called 'The Knowledge.'" You don't have to be outwardly mobile to develop this cognition; mindful meditation shows similar results. What we practice, repeatedly, grows stronger since our brains are plastic, alive, and changing. The networks that we traverse set up intersections where we come together and, at times, collide.

When predetermined paths aren't adequate, pedestrians improvise to find more desirable routes, wearing down groundcover and making new trajectories. Sometimes called "desire lines," some of these paths even result in new crosswalks. In 2006 in San Francisco, artist Anne Divine followed such desire lines when she witnessed the need for crosswalks at an intersection on Sixteenth Street where increasing foot and car traffic posed dangers. At the time in San Francisco, pedestrians accounted for 41 percent of traffic fatalities compared with the national average of 13 percent. The artist walked the equivalent of a marathon in a continuous rectangular pattern to draw attention to paths that pedestrians were regularly taking to get to the other side. To Divine's surprise, her "Crosswalk Marathon" led the city to install new crosswalks.

Divine's crosswalk project derives from a tradition of "walking art." This is not to be confused with "crosswalk art," where neighborhoods embellish their crosswalks as curiosities on pavement; nor are these art installations like Sol Lewitt's *Lines in Two Directions* (1988-1995) at Minneapolis' Walker Art Museum (whose name is a coincidence—not a pun.) For walking artists like Richard Long and Hamish Fulton, their medium found its form through field work. Fulton once described walking as transforming one's state of mind. "I see walking as my form of meditation," he said. "If we were going into the mountains and there was no trail, then we wouldn't be able to think very much, because we would be paying attention to not breaking an ankle or falling over," while walking a trail can "stop the endless thinking mind" so you can "stop going down the same neural pathways." Walking and related embodied navigations (not necessarily on foot but also in wheelchairs and other methods) grow our ability to think as we come into contact with diverse perceptions and perspectives. These experiences arguably generate new crosswalks in our brains.

A range of artists have traversed this aesthetic terrain, opening new possible paths through increasing points of access. In *Blind Field Shuttle*, the artist Carmen Papalia leads non-visual public walking tours, engaging alternative sensory perceptions (smell, sound, touch) by passing useful navigational information to the person behind him, who passes that information down the line. In *Walking and Mapping: Artists as Cartographers*, artist Karen O'Rourke describes how "our gait is as personal as a fingerprint, and so are our multiple itineraries." Walking tracks our itineraries, marked in hindsight on a map or in words, or connected in memory. Writing, like a crosswalk, lays down lines to connect points and invites others to follow (or to detour through alternative desired routes).

To "think like a crosswalk," then, follows networked lines of thought. The literal and metaphoric blend may seem less organic than a mountain, a zebra, or a forest; but like honeycomb from a hive-mind, the metaphor suggests a communal product of passage.

"Human concepts are not just reflections of an external reality," writes philosopher Mark Johnson and linguist George Lakoff in *Metaphors We Live By*; "they are crucially shaped by our bodies and brains, especially by our sensorimotor system." Considering our networked intellectual maps tangling with painted lines that web a city, my metaphor of crosswalks migrates between bodies and landscapes to return to a question that started this essay: How do we think communally (like bees, trees, zebras) to build new crosswalks in our brains?

Future Crosswalks

With cognitive implications, the future of crosswalks lies with our interdependent modes of transport, urban planning, and environmental ecology. This unknown future seems indivisible from cars, whether driven or self-driving. Ian Bogost, who teaches Media Studies at Georgia Tech, hypothesizes: "Once autonomous vehicles are everywhere, letting humans share the roads as pedestrians, bicyclists, or drivers could be seen as too dangerous. Driving conventions like traffic lights and dedicated turn lanes could become obsolete, and transit could develop into a pretzeled web of robotics that no human brain can navigate." While different projections of the future diverge and collide, crosswalks seem to be an increasing part of the plan. As cities have sprawled into suburbs amid cycles of urban blight and renewal, landscape planners have worked to integrate mechanisms for pedestrian flow back toward their centers. In landscapes like Las Vegas, characterized by strip malls, the consequences of lack of flow have led to reassessing the city, planning for more pedestrian thoroughfares, public transport options, walkability measures, and sustainable designs. Las Vegas' new plan for 2045 includes more green networks, bike paths, and crosswalks. Other cities are developing "shared spaces" that aim to redesign the ways streets operate, reducing car traffic to encourage drivers to better accommodate pedestrians. In New York City, the addition of crosswalks and pedestrian features on Queens Boulevard recently expunged its nickname as the "Boulevard of Death." The Netherlands now has glow-in-the-dark crosswalks, and designers in India have developed a 3D crosswalk. In London, artificial intelligence now powers the prototype for an interactive LED crosswalk. Depending on the situation, this crosswalk changes pattern, size, and direction and is named for a bird: the Starling Crosswalk (although this acronym stands for the rather unavian STigmergic Adaptive Responsive LearnING Crossing). The starling idea was actually inspired by ants, who produce pheromones when they forage, akin to a scented communication that attracts more ants and builds a collective path.

Increasingly, countries are passing laws to curb distracted driving. Many states in the US now include laws that ban texting while driving; fourteen states and the District of Columbia have made it illegal for drivers to use hand-held phones. According to the Centers for Disease Control and Prevention, the current estimate of fatalities from distracted driving in the US is nine per day (sixty-three per week) with one thousand injured (seven thousand per week). In the UK, "paint-on-the-floor pedestrian crossings don't cut it anymore," writes reporter Sian Bradley, and are "outdated, and the cause of 20 incidents a day." But even after the mayor of Los Angeles launched an initiative to eliminate traffic accidents two years ago, there has been an 80 percent rise in pedestrian deaths. For all the protective laws and pedestrian-friendly designs, the "accident" factor remains: human behavior. This includes how we see ourselves as part of a larger whole.

I am not an urban planner, neurologist, politician, or other expert in this tangled subject. Rather, I am a pedestrian: "a person who walks along a road or in a developed area." I follow crosswalks most days. Where there are none, I walk the edges of roads, navigate obstacles, and follow my desire lines if no path lies ahead. This requires looking both ways.

As humans, we are animals. Part of who we are is carried in our DNA, and the other part is shaped by our environment. Our brains and bodies cohabit the planet, living and breathing with other species. We move; we interact; at times, we collide. At rare moments we try to fathom our reasons for existing at this moment in space and time, as tiny blips on this planet circling among the stars.

Crosswalk has accrued more meanings since 1744 when the word emerged to describe crisscrossing paths in a garden. Perhaps we are still in a garden, just larger than we imagine. Crosswalks are in the same infrastructural family as bridges and tunnels, not only for people but also for animals. Ecoducts, animal bridges, wildlife overpasses and underpasses assist animal crossings, more than the "zebra crossings" of urban landscapes. Regardless, their shared function highlights where natural and built barriers overlap. Insurance industry standards have estimated in recent years that animal fatalities from collisions happen once every twenty-six seconds—an estimate deemed low, since it was based on reports only from vehicles that had become disabled, not when someone ran over an animal and kept driving. (Again, it's hard not to think of the joke about the chicken—more the joke's underside: to get to the "other side.") As humans encroach on animal habitats, we increasingly realize that we live among animals. A mountain lion eats a dog in California. A grizzly locks itself in a car in Colorado. Concerns arise as if they were in our habitat, rather than we in theirs. "Us" and "them" have always been slippery categories, as if we could separate ourselves from the animals that we are.

Thinking like a crosswalk acknowledges that we have come to a crossroads of thought about all of these intersections. Even when you look both ways at a crosswalk with a signal to step forward, you can still be hit by something unexpected. Ecological phenomena like trophic cascades occur when a top predator vanishes and causes a ripple effect down the food chain; for instance, self-driving cars may lead to a decrease of roadkill (through the disappearance of the top predator: human drivers), but the resulting increase of a lower level of species (for instance, deer) may lead to overpopulation in an area without ample vegetation to sustain them. We live in a web. On a human level there are other considerations, particularly as we make distinctions between "built" and "wild" terrains. Jourdan Imani Keith, founder of the Urban Wilderness Project, has recommended "Desegregating Wilderness," as she explains: "Desegregating the wilderness requires not only the laws that forbid discrimination but also the reintegration of nearby wilderness where people live… [W]hat if wilderness zigzagged through areas where urban people live? Then accessing the wilderness in our daily lives could be more tangible than wild shadows cast by memory." Perhaps such zigzags of wilderness might be considered a kind of crosswalk. Crisscrossing paths in the larger garden that is the planet.

Each day, people devise new types of crossings: streets, borders, walls. Some crosswalks fall into line with traditional pedestrian paths on pavement; other crosswalks reach toward new intellectual dimensions. Synapses fire with each step. At one point or another, we all arrive at various crossroads and need to decide how and whether and where to cross. Sometimes the lines have been drawn for us; sometimes we need to draw the lines. Others can decide whether or not they want to follow, whether the desire lines will disappear or become so traveled that they will be formally marked and mapped. Sometimes we just need to look for white stripes on pavement or make new footprints in the dirt. Wherever we stand, a crosswalk invites us to look both ways as it always lies between two places: where we have come from and where we might go.

Endnotes

This essay on "Thinking Like a Crosswalk" was first delivered as a talk at the University of Utah's Tanner Humanities Center in Salt Lake City, UT, in March 2018. Sources are listed in order of appearance in the essay. Ailsa Chang and Alissa Walker, "Why Pedestrian Deaths are at a 33-year High and How to Prevent Them," *NPR* (01/03/2018). David Schaper, "Human Errors Drive Growing Death Toll in Auto Crashes," *NPR* (10/20/16). David Schaper, "Unsafe Driving Leads to Jump in Highway Deaths, Study Finds," *NPR* (02/15/2017). Edward Humes, *Door to Door: The Magnificent, Maddening, Mysterious World of Transportation* (New York: HarperCollins, 2016), pp. 131-2. Laurel Wamsley, "Walking in America Remains Dangerous," *NPR* (01/10/17). "Crosswalk," *Oxford English Dictionary Online* (December 2016). Eric Poehler, *The Traffic Systems of Pompeii* (Oxford: Oxford University Press, 2017). Kat Eschner, "A Short History of the Crosswalk," *Smithsonian* (10/31/17). Soumya Karlamangla, "Diagonal walkways put drivers, pedestrians at different cross purposes," *Los Angeles Times* (11/02/2014). Jenni Laidman, "Review: 'The Ghost in My Brain' by Clark Elliott," *Chicago Tribune* (07/09/2015). Stephanie Liou, "Neuroplasticity," *Huntington's Outreach Project for Education, at Stanford* (2010). Aldo Leopold, *A Sand County Almanac and Sketches Here and There* (Oxford: Oxford University Press, 1949), p. 129. Eduardo Kohn, *How Forests Think: Toward an Anthropology Beyond the Human* (Berkeley, CA: University of California Press, 2013). Robert Sapolsky, *Why Zebras Don't Get Ulcers* (New York: W.H. Freeman, 1998), pp. 4-5. Anne Harrington quoted in Brendon Larson, *Metaphors for Environmental Sustainability: Redefining Our Relationship with Nature* (New Haven, CT: Yale University Press, 2011), p. 8. Murtha Baca, ed., "Crosswalks, Mapping, and Database Design," *Introduction to Metadata* (Los Angeles, CA: Getty Research Institute, 2008). Rebecca Solnit, *Wanderlust: A History of Walking* (New York: Penguin, 2001), p. 213. Jody Rosen, "The Knowledge, London's Taxi Driver Test, Puts Up a Fight in the Age of GPS," *New York Times* (11/10/2014). David Gelles, *Mindful Work: How Meditation is Changing Business from the Inside Out* (New York, NY: Houghton Mifflin, 2015), p. 64. Elissa Favero, "Mapping desire lines: from Richard Long's walks to the sinewy paths of smell," *Arcade* (08/05/2014). Melanie Carroll, "For safe crossings, S.F. artists walks," *The Examiner* (09/11/2006). Sarah Cascone, "Crosswalk art threatened by Federal Highway Administration's recommendations," *Artnet News* (02/12/2016). Siri Engberg, "New Sol LeWitt work unveiled on the Walker rooftop," *Walker Art Sightlines* (05/26/2016). Alastair Sooke, "Hamish Fulton wanders the neural pathways," *The Telegraph* (01/17/2012). Amanda Cachia, ed., *What can a body do?* (Haverford, PA: Cantor Fitzgerald Gallery, 2012). Karen O'Rourke, *Walking and Mapping: Artists as Cartographers* (Cambridge, MA: MIT Press, 2013), p. xvii. Mark Johnson and George Lakoff quoted in Larson, *Metaphors for Environmental Sustainability*, p. 6. Ian Bogost, "When Cars Fly: The Future of Getting Around," *The Atlantic* (May 2016), p. 35. City Planning Department, Las Vegas, NV, "Vision 2045: Downtown Las Vegas Masterplan." Project for Public Spaces, "What is Shared Space?" (10/05/2017). Winnie Hu, "No Longer New York City's 'Boulevard of Death,' *New York Times* (12/03/2017). Shaunacy Ferro, "These LED Crosswalks Adapt to Whoever is Crossing," *Mental Floss* (10/18/17). "Distracted driving," Centers for Disease Control and Prevention (06/09/2017). Sian Bradley, "This sensor-packed pedestrian crossing is fit for a modern city," *Wired UK* (10/08/17). Melissa Gaskill, "Rise in roadkill requires new solutions," *Scientific American* (05/16/2013). Malia Wollan, "The End of Roadkill," *The New York Times Magazine* (11/12/2017), p. 62. Jourdan Imani Keith, "Desegregating Wilderness," *Orion* (09/10/2014).

Abby, the Comedian

I'm surprised how long it takes
her heart to stop. Strong old girl. Dr. Murrell
keeps the stethoscope pressed to her ribs.
I lean down in front of her unblinking eyes.

"You're a good dog, Abby," I assure her.
Deb, Denny, and Dr. Murrell agree. "You *are*
a good dog, Abby." A beat or two...he puts
the stethoscope away. Faint gray spots on her

rump I've never noticed. Did they swim up when she
got sick? No, I remember hearing color on the fur
begins in the skin. Denny coughs. "This is
the saddest one—she had such a hard life."

"She found love in the end, though," Dr. Murrell says,
looking down, still petting her, and it's true.
If Abby's life had been a Greek play, technically
it would've been a comedy—but how does

Dr. Murrell know that? Can he feel it through her
still-warm hide shooting off hairs with each pass?
Denny scoops her up and carries her to the truck.
Her stuck-out white paw bounces with each step:

Bye-bye. Bye-bye. Bye-bye. Back at the house,
we wait for Collin to help Denny dig the hole.
"Dr. Murrell seems like a nice guy," I say and (I think
to let me know Dr. Murrell wasn't blowing smoke

or maybe to make me feel better) Denny says,
"Dr. Murrell knew everything about her."

The Window in the Mirror

"They know locks are important," the nurse says when she sees me watching a man, younger than my father, twist the switch of a deadbolt nailed to the wall in the dayroom—one of many locks nailed to the wall. Puzzles that can never be solved. Total fake-outs. A tumbler lock, a sliding door latch, an interior doorknob with its little tongue sticking out...

At the table, a woman, also younger than my father, looms over two big piles of Christmas cards—her face frozen in a silent scream. The nurse explains the woman had been in a car accident, and the part of her brain that managed fear got stuck on ON. Old Christmas cards are the only things that make her feel better.

The woman slowly picks up a card from the left-hand pile, opens it, closes it, then lays it down on the right-hand pile. Her fluid movement reminds me of the Japanese tea ceremony. A flimsy chain tethers her to the chair like a dog no one thinks will run away.

Spratchet

I like the idea of a spratchet,
which today I learned
is the plastic divider
used in checkout lines
that says *this is almost mine*
and *this is almost yours.*
I like how it helps two strangers
not skinny dip in the reservoirs
of each other's bank accounts.
And there's nothing rude about a spratchet—
it's as polite as plastic can possibly be.
Unlike the bolt click behind a door
or the whining hinge of a fence gate,
the spratchet keeps things
only subtly separate.
Gently, the cashier lowers
my oyster crackers into a bag.
He divides the dry from the frozen.
I nod my spratchet nod. At work
I shake with my practiced
spratchet hand. At home,
I put the groceries in the cupboard
and kiss my love, and even our lips
are little spratchets. I cannot know her.
She cannot know me. No matter
how intimate. Not really.
That's what we have to agree on.
That's what I intend on forgetting.

ESTHER LIN

Reading Madame Bovary

That afternoon, Bovary went
to the apothecary's closet,

fumbling for arsenic
to draw out her black bile,

make her mouth a hole.
She waited hours for the worst of it,

the shearing of her dark lovely hair—
though for many years

my mother's hair was not lovely
but thin as sagebrush

an autumn fire had passed over.
There are mothers who demand

a price. Youth. Sex organs
without cancer. She said,

You can't know how bad it is.
Bovary's daughter worked in a satin mill.

There is no talk of her beauty.
To say my mother was not beautiful

when she died is merciless.
Today I am without mercy.

Bent Arrows: On Anticipation of My Approaching Disappearance

They come arching over the horizon from distant places, like bent, crooked arrows dispatched from many directions.

They arrive in thin blue envelopes on folded stationery, or in fat, feverishly duct-taped packages. By overnight mail—sent prepaid by Fed Ex—($26.00!)—containing, say, three little misshapen onyx pebbles, which, I am told, should be placed in the corner of my sleeping room to ward off negative spirits.

A brass Turkish medallion from a person I hardly know, accompanied by a three-page letter explaining how she acquired it in Bulgaria, during her sexually promiscuous 1990s.

An ironed-flat wax paper packet of pressed dried lavender and rosemary from someone's garden in Indiana.

A passionate testimonial to the healing power of spirulina.

A tribute CD of Gay Clark songs.

A handmade cedar-scented candle. A whoopee cushion.

The Irish friend from New Jersey sends a three-hour recording called "Long Healing Prayer"—a nonstop, droning dirge, performed, it seems, by three widows who have broken into the instrument closet of a medieval Celtic monastery. Wailing voices that float endlessly on a slick of fiddle music, like an Irish oil spill. It should be called Suicide Note on Forlorn Bagpipe.

The reason I am the recipient of these exotic attentions is simple: I went on hospice service a month ago, and word leaked out. My cancer is no longer being treated, my narrative is fixed, the time uncertain but not distant. Now acquaintances and friends and even utter strangers are cleaning out their emotional cabinets, like midwives tying an umbilical knot between the dead and the living. Although I am the one dying, it is clear that they are the ones speaking their last words.

*

In a flat, heavy box, three Ziplock baggies, full of sand scooped and labeled from three different beaches: one in Florida, one on Cape Cod, one in Michigan.

From California, a message from the widow of a friend arrives: "I hope the end comes fast for you, as it did for Y."

Person X writes to tell me how good morphine is, and how she hopes those stingy bastards in the medical profession are giving me the good stuff. Her tone is one of barely disguised fury.

Then there is the genre of blithely delivered misinformation: the cheerful note that says, "Heard you are doing much better! So great to hear!"

Not all of the messages are whacky projections. Some are carefully worded, unexaggerated statements of friendship and memory (this turns out to be the essence of the business).

Others are like saturated handkerchiefs, soaked and dripping with sentimentality; monologues in which the mourner is so carried away by her capacity to emote deeply, I feel I should avert my eyes from such a private moment.

Persons I haven't heard from in decades want to visit and renew our friendship. But, isn't it a little late for that, I wonder? I imagine them standing over my couch, looking down at my diminished body, and I wonder what it is that they believe they have to say, what they have to bring, what they imagine they would like to take away. I wonder what they would see.

By email someone else writes, "I've discovered this wonderful anthology: *200 Greatest Zen Death Poems!* I'm sending them to you immediately."

I drift on my polka dot couch, I read and write. I watch the ceiling and the skies, and the strange missives—some touching, some bizarre—arrive. People I once considered close evaporated months ago; others, whom I thought as peripheral, have appeared and stayed: sane, stalwart and present. Their voices are oddly reassuring. Most of the time now, dying doesn't seem like such a big thing.

How do you feel? I sometimes ask myself, not really knowing.

*

I have this image: I am floating on my back on a great body of water, buoyed comfortably by some kind of life vest. My gaze on the sky; seagulls and birds drift high overhead, on their way elsewhere; the clouds keep changing. I feel lonely, but calm. This is not so bad, I think. This sensation, of being held up by water, is something I have always loved.

In the distance, I can see the huge ocean liner from which I seem to have fallen overboard. With its many, many remaining passengers, it is moving away from me. Soon it will be out of sight. A ship that size, I understand, is simply too big to turn around for one person.

Even so, I can still glimpse the figures of people standing at the stern railing of that great ship—my friends—and in addition, some other people I don't recognize. Over the railing they are tossing bouquets, messages in bottles, pieces of chocolate cake in Tupperware containers; old photographs, bundles of dried sage. These are their goodbyes, their farewell gifts.

Once in a while, something splashes with a thunk and a ripple into the water near me. I am the passive participant in these transactions. No response is required of me. And these strange bent arrows keep arriving.

I gaze up at the endlessly interesting, endlessly changing sky.

Here comes another. There it goes.

I think someone is looking for me.

GAIL MAZUR

Blue Work Shirt

I go into our bedroom closet
with its one blue work shirt, the cuffs

frayed, the paint stains a loopy non-
narrative of color, of spirit.

Now that you are bodiless
and my body's no longer the body you knew,

it's good to be reminded every morning
of the great mess, the brio of art-making.

—On the floor, the splattered clogs
you called your "Pollock shoes."

KERRIN McCADDEN
Losing

My brother is lost. I can't find my brother. I say it over again—
when I lost my brother. A back road I knew once and now

can't find. A specific wave on John's Pond. The last one we saw
there, the blue-lipped sleep of overdose. He goes from one

office to the next, and no one will return my calls. One day
he was somewhere. I know he must have been. The difference

in weight between alive and dead. Do the old experiment again.
Weigh the escaped soul. Let it have gone somewhere. Let it

have packed one bag. Is my brother any amount of atoms at all,
fending for themselves? If I keep saying, *I have lost my brother,*

is there a corollary? Do I make way-finding? A compass,
a geocache, a crashed plane on his island, his black box full

of laughter? Every next syllable said by everyone is my brother.
Silent mouths—these are where dead brothers live. I keep

a jar of nails like a bouquet of denial. Life ends with us finding
leaves underfoot. Fend for ourselves, I'm saying. There is music

everywhere. There must be a bit of his breath left. Put the needle
in the track again. My brother, somewhere, knows the tune.

Anatomy Practical

I am searching for the phrenic nerve
when I remember the bad feeling I have about you.

Formalin pricking my nose, an attentive hush pressing all around me.
This test is timed, but
I look into the body, and I'm lost.

The word itself makes me anxious,
sounds frantic, frenetic.
Lightning strike climbing up beside the heart.

Now my eyes won't focus, and I remember
sleeping, head on your chest on the airport floor, how my dreams
were full of rhythms: a locked door and someone knocking
with a strange kind of urgency—
steady but ceaseless.

At the same time I notice the fingernails
on the bloodless hands, yet undissected,
are painted pink.

And the timer sounds.

The Age of Migration

Charley sponges off the dinner dishes—hers and Karim's, the girl's, the Goat's—then slots them one by one into the rack to drip. All the while staring straight ahead through her reflection into the night. Despite the heat, unusual for Paris in late October, she keeps the windows latched against police sirens and Maghrebi rap and air pollution: level orange again. But there's no defense against the soccer match blaring from the next room where Karim and his pal are smoking Turkish tobacco and drinking mint tea.

"Are you trying to wake up the kids?" she says, passing through the murky salon toward the bedroom. "If not, could you turn it down some?"

Karim flashes her his 100-watt smile, white teeth set off by the glossy frame of a new black beard, eyes crinkling with sympathy. Otherwise, he doesn't budge. Probably he didn't hear her.

In the bedroom, Charley navigates by city glow, the soft aura of traffic lights and illumination from high-rises surrounding this one.

Bracing her arms on either side of the crib, she leans down to inhale the warm bread-and-oil scent of Sami's head. Her mouth ajar to savor more deeply, as cats do. Nothing in the world smells as wonderful as her ten-month-old boy. "Here's how you'll grow up in this ghetto of Seine-Saint-Denis, little one." It's an exhaled thought, an inverted benediction, less than a whisper. "You'll dump the useless school and learn to deal drugs. You'll prey on girls. You'll get hauled up in court and released the same day. You'll look at me with the same blank eyes as the dropouts who watch us down in the streets. You'll be out of my reach."

On a floor mattress to the left of the parents' bed lies Rachida, Karim's six-year-old niece, curled into a question mark. From their first meeting, Charley has tried to fill the empty place in Rachida's motherless heart.

She holds her breath to hear theirs. Rachida, dreaming, emits snorts and starts, while the baby's sighs arrive almost imperceptibly, like lapping waves.

*

Maiwenn lifted Charley's hand in hers, to peel open the clenched fingers. Maiwenn's nails were manicured, Charley's jagged. She has never comprehended manicures.

"You're not an egotist, chérie. You are the *opposite*. You'll be *rescuing* them. It will take courage for a little time. OK. But afterward comes the rest of your life. And theirs!"

"But Rachida's not even my own—"

"No. But Dennis promised to arrange for her too. Didn't he?"

"Um." Charley looked away, past her baby carriage to the tree-studded cliffs of the Buttes Chaumont park. A miniature Alpine wilderness on the outskirts of the city, only a twenty-minute bus ride from her gritty, concrete neighborhood. Hard to believe it had become the HQ of fundamentalist terrorists, but that's what one heard, and not only on the internet.

Maiwenn clasped Charley's hand. "Dennis is an American. *And* an attorney. He has an air like Clooney, no? OK, laugh! Little idiot, he would die for you! Doesn't the man realize he could have any chick in Paris? Maybe he's an idiot too. But if you don't believe *Dennis*—"

Charley lifts the scarf from the bureau and drapes it around her head as best she can, as the Goat himself insisted on teaching her, right after Karim brought it home. She fumbles with the pins and the slithery cloth, afraid of waking one of the children.

Pulling the bedroom door shut, she announces, "I have to go down. We're almost out of diapers. I'll be quick." Go down: fourteen stories to the Proxi market. If the elevator is working.

The Goat says, "Come here so I can fix that hijab. You actually look ridiculous."

The Goat is in his forties, green-eyed with a wispy grizzled beard. He is only a self-proclaimed theologian, not a real imam. His visits began soon after Charley moved in with Karim, months before the baby, and now as if he were a blood relative, he's completely at ease seeing and touching Charley's shining mahogany curls, while teaching her how to hide them.

Karim says, "Let her go, the Goat. What matters is, she's halal. Right? Good girl."

Take that, she thinks. *See? We're a couple.* Karim has always understood her, deep down. He glanced at her—checking her over before letting her enter the public space—but now his gaze reverts to the Samsung wide-screen, where black and white men with muscular thighs are zigzagging around each other. She waits, pulse pounding in her throat, wanting him to turn and see her again. Completely. To smile again.

Wanting him not to turn.

"Need anything? Sure not? I'm off then." Her tongue sticks. She coughs words out like broken eggshells, while one hand pushes down the door latch.

"Wait!"

A bird of prey comes hurtling toward her. His obsidian eyes. His sandalwood perfume. "Here, silly habibi." Euros thrust into her hand. "You forgot to ask for money."

Maiwenn is independent in her life and in her mind. She admits no obligations to anyone. Her adoption never took, she says; their sole moment of mutual joy was seeing the last of each other. Maiwenn draws eyes everywhere, with her blond hair in cornrows (hell to braid, she says, but easier to keep clean where there's no water), Nefertiti neck, and large, mobile features ever so slightly flattened, as if the artist who drew her had wiped his sleeve over the page. She's a connoisseur of designer labels, foie gras, and champagne, who lives on pennies. She teaches self-defense freelance, and helps manage humanitarian missions all over the world. She could organize hell itself. Charley has never seen her cry nor heard her complain. The darker things look, the more raucous Maiwenn's laughter.

Maiwenn at thirty-six is everything Charley would wish to be, while Charley, just twenty-three, has everything Maiwenn wants. Parents who give a damn. A Sorbonne degree. A man who doesn't cheat on her: find me another one of *those* in Paris! And a child.

Why, then, only last week, did Maiwenn again insist on Charley leaving?

"Because I want something *more* for you, ma 'tite."

"Go on. You want more for me than for yourself?"

"Shit, when you put it that way..." A soft chuckle. "But absolutely *yes*! I do." Leaning into the pram that she insisted on pushing as if Charley were sick, "True, my little cabbage?" And then, straightening up, "Besides, don't you see? Your relationship is not only going nowhere at this point. It's getting dangerous."

"Oh, *please*." But Charley's eyes aren't scornful. They're riveted on Maiwenn's perfectly lipsticked mouth, waiting for her friend's next words.

"It's not only Karim, cherie. Life as we know it is about to explode. *Daesch* is getting its ass kicked in Syria, you think that's so good? Wait. The volunteer jihadi from France will come running back home. All trained up. Or—" she glanced around with a glinting grin. "They're here, already."

Charley reached to take back the carriage. "Paris isn't Aleppo. We have laws. And trained-up police."

Summoned from the top floor, the elevator shudders out of its coma. A narrow cylinder, an upright fluorescent coffin that she ducks into quickly, jabbing the ground floor button. The hurky-jerky descent is agonizing. Through the glass door she sees a cluster of boys on the tenth-floor landing, dealing drugs or shaking down apartment dwellers or both. On the third, a family of clandestines huddles under bright filthy quilts despite the heat.

Appear, disappear.

In the still intact sliver of elevator mirror she encounters a stranger. Defined by the hijab her face looks round as a peach, more youthful. The lips full and pale, brows arched high over half-closed eyes, all serenely concealing the storm inside her. She tucks the scarf's folds tighter.

"Really? You brought me a present?"

Karim held out a white bag tied with a red bow, embossed with a logo she didn't recognize. The expression on his face wavered as if seen through water. She'd seen that look on him once before, when he presented her with the Swarovski ring. The ring flashed now as she dug in the tissue paper to draw out, like a stage magician, a long piece of grainy yet slithery cloth.

"A scarf? It's—really fantastic. Thank you!" A hideous color. The beige of dead flesh. Go on, kiss him thank-you. "Thank you, my love."

"As I promised, habibi. Your first hijab. Silk jersey, the best. Here, let's see it on!" He studied her, then stroked her cheek. "Do this little thing I ask. Not for you, for me. Although soon, you won't want to be without it. Else you'll feel naked out on the street." Now he smiled, as if at a joke between them.

Later she would ask herself over and over: what is the difference between wearing a ring and wearing a hijab? A riddle that seemed trivial at first.

When she first met Karim he scoffed at what he called the third monotheism, which he blamed for turning the Arab civilization, after its glorious flowering of art and mathematics, into a repressive theocracy ripe for colonial takeover. Around his family he sang a different song, but would she have wanted him to disrespect his parents? And any twinges of misgiving Charley may have felt about putting on the ring were swept away by her own parents, old-time lefties over the moon at the prospect of an alliance between their daughter and a politically active son of the immigration.

Two years ago, as they walked arm in arm in the forest of Vincennes, Charley told Maiwenn: "My folks don't care that he's jobless. I swear they see me as their personal reparation for the Algerian War. Like the Catholics buying an indulgence for their sins. Shouldn't I feel angry? Instrumentalized? But you know what? I love to see them happy about me, even if—"

Maiwenn reached to tap Charley's head lightly. "You and your overintellectualizing! Anyway, it's not like you two are getting married. It's only the civil contract. For your protection, so he can't just walk out. I mean, suppose you get pregnant?"

"Not a chance. I said, he hasn't got a *job*."

"With his looks he'll soon find one. Besides, I think you're in love?"

Charley looked down at her rough nails. She felt the opposite of a blush: all the blood had drained suddenly from her face. That thing

Karim and she made together, that fusion, a long explosion of light *like a star being born*, yes, so they both agreed—so overwhelming that for days afterward she would avoid touching, even looking at him, not wanting to inadvertently arouse his desire. Because she wasn't whole again yet.

In the lobby the lights are smashed out. Shards of glass sparkle everywhere, fallen stars. The blue rotors of a fleet of police cars bloom on the walls. She nearly goes flying when her foot rolls over a bottle on the ground.

The Proxi's narrow aisles overflow with canned goods, soft drinks, chips, soap, diapers, rotting plantains, all the necessities of ghetto life. She stumbles over the crates and pallets and hands the Tunisian a five-euro bill in exchange for the powder-blue suitcase stowed behind his counter.

Money is the least of her worries. There are two thousand euros in crisp fifties hidden in her Lancel purse. She used to keep all her stuff— books, snacks, makeup—in an old backpack, but in Maghrebi culture it's a man's honor to dress his woman well. She, Karim, Rachida, and the baby live in a three-room dump, but her dress and leggings come from the Galerie Lafayette.

When did their life begin to change course? In little increments like degrees on a compass, and too gradually for Charley to put her finger on any starting point.

While Charley was pregnant, Karim started taking free Arabic lessons (her Sorbonne version was hopelessly academic, he said, incomprehensible to real people) and studying the Koran in translation, as well as philosophers such as Al-Farabi and Ibn Arabi. "Pure curiosity," he assured her. "They're amazing, the convergence of mysticism and rationality. *You* should read these guys! And by the way, how would you have me live day to day, habibi? Standing in line like a dumb statistic for a job that doesn't exist? Or expanding my mind?"

After Sami was born the Goat dropped by daily to take Karim down to the pubs where women were considered haram, to smoke chichi. There was an androgynous quality about the theologian, with his long striped robe and fluid movements. Perhaps that was the reason for his unflattering nickname: she'd heard older Arabs who couldn't bother with their wives' names refer to them generically as "the Goat."

His closeness and the reek of perfumed tobacco while he was jerking the fold of the beige cloth into place had made her stomach churn. As he looped the generous swath of cloth over her chest she realized that purpose of the hajib was as much to conceal her cleavage, the pride of every Frenchwoman, as her hair.

"I feel like I'm in transformation," she joked apologetically to Dennis the first time he saw her wearing the scarf. "Someone who used to be one thing and isn't yet another. Wrapped like a pupa in this beige cocoon."

Wheeling the suitcase to the next corner, out of sight of the Tunisian, hugging close to her building to stay invisible from high above. Scanning the flow of cars and vans and cycles. If her driver doesn't get here soon Karim and/or the Goat will come down to hunt for her, instantly bloody-minded, ready to set fire to the neighborhood if that's what it takes.

Nervousness can blind you. There's the black Opel, waiting patiently all along, its tail lights blinking. The driver, nearly as shiny black as his car, leaps out as she steps forward.

"Abdul?"

"Caroline?" he responds, already reaching for the suitcase. She's reminded of the opening scene of Hamlet. *Stand, ho! Who's there?* Thank Uber for bringing intrigue back into the everyday world.

The car jolts into traffic, throwing Charley/Caroline back into its puffy leather embrace. She doesn't dare look up until they've crossed the frontier of the burb of Seine-Saint-Denis into Paris proper.

What has she forgotten?

She ticks off in her mind:

> Cellphone
> Passport
> Cash
> Underwear
> Sweaters, jacket

Clothes she was no longer allowed to wear
Toothbrush, face cleanser, creams, tampons
Contraceptives.

What has she forgotten? What?

"Darling. Darling. *Darling*." Dennis pulls her from the car into his arms. His lips graze lightly over her face, stippling kisses. Behind him rolls the indigo Seine. The air tastes fizzy-clean here in the seventh arrondissement, home to ministries, museums, and the extremely well-heeled.

He tugs at her scarf. "You can lose this now. Ugh. What a nightmare."

"Oh. I forgot." She stuffs it into her bag.

"And what's this?" Caressing her back pocket. "Oh Christ. Your cellphone, are you crazy? Sweetheart, give me that, they're probably already using it to find you—" He half-turns, manipulating the phone's controls. "There. I killed the GPS. But just in case—" With a baseball player's spin he lobs her phone over the stone parapet into the river. "Hasta la vista! We'll buy you another one tomorrow."

"I don't care." She feels mystified.

"My brave girl. You did it. You're here, safe!"

"You didn't trust me?"

"*You*, of course. But I was going nuts, you can ask your friend. I wasn't sure. Not until this moment. Come on, she's waiting up in my place..."

He runs over the plan again as they walk. They will leave for New York tomorrow. He will set gears in motion to gain asylum for her, and while those wheels grind away, direct the French authorities to reunite mother and child. And why not try for the orphaned girl? After all, isn't she at risk of female mutilation, given the nest of fundamentalists holding her captive?

Rachida's future sounds less sure than Charley had thought. Don't start thinking, idiot. Hug Maiwenn instead, inhale her cologne, twirl this glass of champagne. When is the last time you drank alcohol? Absorb this fabulous living room: the designer lighting, the rose satin sofa and chairs, the glass tables. You were only here twice before. The last time two months ago. Before or after the Goat started having you followed? Or following you himself.

"How do you expect me to convert? 'Convert' means to turn from one thing to something else. I've never been *anything*."

"You are Catholic of course. You're French."

She threw the Goat a look meant to wither. He shrugged.

Karim stretched his long limbs, rotated his head. It was high summer. He hadn't changed out of his polyester team soccer shorts and shirt, the shin pads and cleats. "Listen, habibi. You don't have to convert. You don't have to believe anything. Faith doesn't enter by force, right?"

Charley wanted to cry out hallelujah, to throw herself on Karim's gleaming sweaty chest right in front of the Goat.

"All you need to do is *behave* like a good Muslim. Then we'll see what develops."

"Or not."

"How does that Beatles song go? 'Smile and you'll feel happy?'"

"Wrong, my love. It's from Charlie Chaplin." Had he forgotten she was nicknamed after the silly little actor? "It goes, 'Smile, though your heart is aching…'"

"Dum, dum de dum da de dah," the Goat hummed the tune. Karim and Charley ignored him.

"To act the part?" she asked Karim. "That's really all you expect from me?"

"That's all."

The Goat fumed.

Charley grinned. "You know I won't set foot in a mosque. Not in a million years."

"No *problem*, habibi!"

Why not act the part, then? Like most French teenagers she'd grown up movie-struck, had taken a few courses in acting before reality sunk in. So why not play the good Muslim woman, enjoy the fun in it? Learn to cook halal from Karim's suddenly affable mother, try out the novelty of wearing a skirt over long pants, go to the hammam to be scrubbed and oiled while enjoying the gossip of the other women. At last putting her Arab language study to practical use.

After that first shock, even the hijab became possible. All part of learning her role.

Is Maiwenn wearing more makeup than usual? No, it's her rising blood suffusing her cheeks like a rash. A spilled dash of champagne sizzles on the rug as she lifts her glass to Charley's "feminist backbone." She winks at Dennis. Her English is colloquial, if not always grammatical. "Learned in the field," she says with a wink, "not at the pillow." Now she launches into the details of how she will manage Karim, commiserate with him, insist on watching the children so he can do whatever he needs to do—thus she will flush out his plans. Don't worry, you two. You'll win.

Charley nods, bowled over by Maiwenn's gift for reducing mountains to sand castles. But this is someone who organizes shipments of tents, medicine, and even doctors to war zones. Protecting a pair of children will be, so to speak, child's play.

"Take it down a notch, Maiwenn," says Dennis. "We're infinitely grateful for your help. But this is not a game."

The first time Charley entered this apartment, she knew she would sleep with its owner. They both knew, without saying a word. They had met a month earlier, when he belatedly joined the business French course she taught at AngloFrango. Dennis Altman irritated her: another foreign big shot above learning the basics, and it would be her responsibility to save him from flunking.

In the fabulous apartment, she first checked for signs of a resident female. An empty space on a shelf where a photo had been removed, or a lingering scent, or some overlooked bathroom article. Not out of jealousy—that would be absurd. She had no emotions for the American. It was only because she didn't want to raid another woman's life merely to satisfy an inexplicable drive. Which was what? Pure curiosity? Or awakened vanity? Each time he invited her for coffee he slathered on compliments about her eyes, "brilliant as topaz," her slender hands, her underused intelligence, her wit. When for the first time she turned up wearing the hijab, his knobby face fell to pieces. It's a crime, he said hoarsely, a crime to cover your beautiful hair.

She was drying her hands in his bathroom when he knocked. Through the closed door he offered to draw her a bath in the Jacuzzi. She laughed *yes*; this was so unexpected, and so welcome, after a day's teaching in hot July (the same week, she recalls now, as the gift of the hijab). He watched her as she lay in the bath letting the jets play on her like little hands. His close scrutiny was surprisingly arousing. She had just stopped breast-feeding and her breasts were still full. In his bedroom she came only moments after his pale sex entered her. Then he heaved over her like a sail in the wind. With his tears dropping on her neck he lifted her hair in one hand and ran a lock through his open mouth.

Resting her head on Dennis Altman's shoulder, inhaling the vinegar smell of his older man's body, Charley dug deep inside herself for the backlash of guilt. For a paralyzing twinge of remorse. She found nothing. There had been a moment of physical release, forgettable and for that reason unregrettable. It happened in a universe light-years from the one she and Karim made together.

Now as she sips and listens to the others, the apartment asks: was it betrayal you came looking for here?

Charley approaches the full-length, east-facing window. A lawn of lights twinkles to the horizon. Beyond lies invisible Seine-Saint-Denis.

Maiwenn touches her cheek. "Whatever it is, you better get over it."

Dennis comes up on her left. Three reflections lined up in the window. "Darling. You know it's now or never. I'm an attorney, not a miracle-worker. With this clown in the White House, it's getting tougher week by week to bring non-citizens in. And with your set of relationships here? Ouch. Fingers crossed nobody digs too deep."

Karim was going to the mosque every Friday. He unrolled his prayer mat five times a day in the bedroom. Three weeks ago, beaming, he told her their marriage party was scheduled for mid-November. The Goat, managing the details, constantly reminded Karim that the Prophet preached against long engagements.

"The *Prophet* is so irrelevant to us. Wait. Will there be an imam there?"

"Of course."

"An imam! Karim, no! I said *never*. And you promised, shit, you agreed!"

Karim put his hands on her shoulders. He ordered her down on her knees.

Charley found herself obeying, with a shiver of arousal that left her shaken.

"The Goat told me to beat you if you made a fuss. But I can't do that, habibi. I love you way too much."

Her forehead rubbed the gritty floor. Not now, but when? So the Goat had not told him her secret. Because he only had suspicions? Or in order to be able later to hold that much more power over her?

Maiwenn's phone plays Pink Martini's "Je ne veux pas travailler…" She squints at the screen. "Oh the fuck. It's him."

"Karim? Calling *you*?" With a shaking hand Charley sets her champagne flute down to safety on a glass table. "Already?"

"Power that damn thing off!" Dennis reaches for Maiwenn's phone.

Maiwenn, who is a good six centimeters taller, holds it high overhead. "I did. And hands off! Don't you tell *me* what to do."

"If that madman turns up here now it will be your fault."

"So leave!"

Charley sinks to a crouch on the white tile. "Please. Don't argue, please!" A child begging her parents to reconcile. How pathetic. Her own parents, who never argued, who to her always seemed melted together like wax, would be devastated to see her in this fabulous apartment, having left her family, about to run away with a rich American. In silence she suddenly cries out to them, *It's your fault that I'm here. I need my freedom too!*

Maiwenn hauls her upright and hugs her close. Breasts crushing breasts. Charley wants Maiwenn's arms to be around her forever.

Dennis and Charley taxi to the airport Hilton. For what will remain of the night. Charley dozes, waking every hour or so with a sense of a trapdoor flying open beneath her. Can she do this? Must she? If it is about her freedom—and yes, that *is* the question, not vanity, not lust, not boredom—couldn't there be another way?

She sees herself back in the park with Maiwenn, again. A week ago. A world ago. Rachida and Sami were happily grubbing in the sandbox, laughing at each other.

"Suppose," said Charley, fumbling for words. "Suppose Karim is simply being...honest. With me. OK, right now he's asking me to help him lead a more traditional life. As an enlightened seeker. Why not? Islam doesn't equal radical 'islamism.' You'd be the first person to say so."

Maiwenn leaned very close, frowning. "One thing I *detest* is sentimentality. Believe me, Karim is heading down a one-way street. If you want to stay, stay! Follow him! But with eyes wide open, either way. Because if once you trick him and leave and are ever stupid enough to come back—"

She broke off. No need for an ending.

Karim never suspected. Never smelled a thing, literally, because she showered every trace off her skin before going home. But somehow the Goat smelled her deception. After the Goat began having her followed, she stopped meeting Dennis. From then on they only communicated through Maiwenn. Like Romeo and Juliet, connecting through the friar. What would she have done without Maiwenn? She'd have been trapped forever.

But tonight Karim is out looking for her. By now he will know of her crime. A crime in his view, in its classical outlines—this time around, Iago, a.k.a. the Goat, didn't lie. And if Karim were to find her? What would he do, in his pain and fury?

The children are safe, she tells herself. No one hurts children. Soon the authorities will take custody of them. Dennis promised. I'll have Sami back in my arms before he takes his first step. If I've harmed anyone, it's Rachida. The girls lose. But Rachida's not mine.

They're flying business class. The exclusive express line for passport control trots swiftly through the rat's maze of rope barriers, leaving no time to drag one's feet. Dennis gives her a firm squeeze as if to say, good girl, brave girl, you can do this! The uniformed policeman behind his Plexiglas window rifles through her passport to bestow its first exit stamp. Bang! She is through, right behind Dennis.

If he weren't leading the way Charley would be lost. Broad corridors lead in all directions, gleaming bright. A sleek railway runs to the gate hub, the security check where she must strip off random bits of clothing, then aisles of gold-bright shops: Hermes, Dior, Lancel.

Groups of heavily made-up women wearing vanilla-colored hijab and long tunics scout for luxuries.

In Seine-Saint-Denis some wives defy the law by wearing the black, suffocating, face-concealing, mobile prison called a niqab. Charley didn't pity them. They scared her. In France the face-covering veil was banned in 2011. She clung to that fact when Karim brought home a complicated dark garment for her to model. *Hush. It's only to try, habibi.*

No one can be *forced* to wear the niqab! French women are the most educated and emancipated in the world. Thanks to the bloody battles of the Revolution. Thanks to heroes like Simone de Beauvoir, and Simone Weil, and, yes, her parents' generation, the old lefties… Her heart is near bursting. Is this some sort of schoolgirl patriotism? Maiwenn would laugh at her for sure.

Or perhaps not.

"Where are you going?" Dennis catches the crook of her elbow.

"I don't *know*!" But like a dog straining against her leash she rears back toward where she came from.

In the plane a voice announces that the doors have closed. They will be taking off shortly. Expected flight time is eight hours. The weather in New York is 11 degrees Celsius, 52 Fahrenheit. "An honest-to-God fall at last," sighs Dennis, buckling her in. "You will *love* Central Park in autumn."

Three things happen.

First, she remembers what it is that she forgot. The photographs. Because now that her phone is sunk deep in the Seine, she has no photos of Sami. Or Maiwenn. Or of anyone.

Next, her chin is nudged by Dennis to raise up for his kiss. It is not an amorous kiss, but a slow press against her lips like a seal on a document. When he pulls back, his face is transfigured. Tears magnify his blue eyes. "Never," he says. "Never in my life have I been truly happy. Until now."

Charley's heart twists. She is the opposite of free. She is the cause of this man's terrible happiness.

A stewardess offers champagne from a tray.

Casually, as if she had dropped something, Charley reaches down into her purse to wrap her hand tightly into the hijab.

*

They are airborne! She scarcely felt it happen. Like childbirth under anesthesia, she thinks. Maiwenn would like that one. The stewardess exchanges her empty glass for a menu decorated with a red ribbon. The stewardesses wear their hair rolled into chignons tight as Minerva's helmet. Charley must learn that hairdo. With her mahogany curls spilling over her shoulders, swinging when she moves, she feels half naked. As in one of those dreams where you're walking in a crowd in daylight wearing only panties, and all you can do is put on a bold face.

"You look tired, darling. A tiny siesta before dinner?" Dennis leans over Charley to demonstrate the controls: the movies, the book light, buttons for moving one's self upright, halfway or flat. He tucks a quilt over her legs. She realizes that she's been shivering in the air-conditioning.

Business class is a strange concept: each passenger is enclosed on three sides by a plastic cage of his or her own. Once her bed is lowered, she and Dennis can barely see each other over the edges of their individual shells.

She pulls the scarf out of her purse and drapes it across her eyes as a shield against the light. Yes, to cut the light, that's all. She doesn't weep into the cloth that smells of herself. Maiwenn would despise that. But every cell in her body is seeping microscopic tears, while in the dark world created by her scarf the jet engines pulse like a lullaby for the stars she imagines them flying up to meet...

"Oh, for Chrissake!"

Dennis' voice startles her awake.

"That damned headcloth again? I don't believe it. We'll give this rag—" He tugs the scarf up and away with a barking laugh. "A ceremonial burning in New York."

Dazzled by the overhead lights, Charley reaches blindly.

"Hold on, darling! Let me get your flight kit open. What you want is—" Sound of an opening zipper. He circles her wrist, prods something into her hand. "Now isn't that better?"

Her fingers rub over cotton cloth, elastic bands.

"It's your eye-mask! If you don't like the color, we can change it—"

Charley struggles to sit upright. The seatbelt holds her on the flat bed.

Dennis kisses her rigid knuckles. "Relax, darling. Here! Now let me see you put it on."

MAGGIE MILLNER
Magical Thinking

There was some connection to be made—
your death, the election, the absurd snow—
and I charged myself with making it, walking
down Court Street after therapy, passing under
mantled elms, watching the skaters' ankles
brace against the weight of their careening.

In the rink's center, a girl spun herself into a small
torpedo, red coat flaring conical, dark hat poking out
like a singed wick. She was likely half my age
though it was clear she possessed something already
I had no hope of ever developing. My lot was to watch—
to lift the velvet rope and lead her image through

the darkly papered corridor of thought and record
the way it changed what preexisted it. As I started
south, the fat flakes hardened into white gravel. Poison
wafted off the newsstands in vaporous wings.
With every step, I felt the girl complete another turn
inside me, flung on by her own centrifugal will.

Because I couldn't stand to face the other figures
in my mind, I studied her the whole walk home—
her thrown head, cinched laces, her skate etching
language into me with its bright blade. When I fit
my house key in the lock, her spinning slowed. When
I passed your photo on the wall, it started up again.

To the Old Man Who Lived on a Hill

He was looking for news of the world. He was looking for his daughter
who died in the fire, the car that burst into flames, the crash, his wife
who left him for her lover, he was looking

at the world through a window in the den, where he kept the photographs
and the heater, the air conditioner and the dog treats, the trophies
from spelling bees and dance recitals. He was looking at how light changed

the texture of shadows, petals on the lawn. Spring is ending here,
and dust collects on rows of encyclopedias lining the shelves,
on the heavy crucifix hanging on the wall. It is morning,

it is night. The television flickers, muted: documentary, documentary,
pornography, documentary, the news. I was hired to give him a reason
to live, and to rid the kitchen of its spoiled food, to clean

the animal droppings from the dogs, from the bird that would get in
through the basement, to persuade him to sleep in his bed, and not
on the plastic covered mattress in the guest room. His back ached.

There is sadness and then there is the thing beyond sadness.
4:00 a.m. infomercials, roaches marching over the expanse
of cracked walls, trying to masturbate and finding you cannot,

wanting your dogs to love you, and knowing they will eat you
when you die. You could learn to change, you could learn
to apologize, you think, if given the chance—

For a few hours of work I collect $70 a day,
talk about the weather, dogs, politics. I take the rotting food
and replace it with green things. I watch his face animate,

change, go blank for hours in the afternoon. Then
a thought slides down, like morning dew on spider silk—
it lingers for a moment, it tries to transform itself.

MEGAN PINTO
The Unfolding

I let a boy lick my paper skin because he told me
I was pretty. I let a man undress me, because he wouldn't
stop kissing me. I left my body at a party, and then
I left it again. A secret: sadness has no sound—not crying,
just silence, like how at 5:00 a.m. I woke up in the middle
of Brooklyn in the back of a cab, the driver watching me.

I learned to love with nobody watching—in a carpeted room,
small, my bed in the corner, while outside tall trees blocked out
a blinding sun. God moves in the laying on of hands. A child
shivers in a church, her body wet with water. Then someone
holds her, warms her, blesses her. I miss Raleigh in the winter,

I miss Ohio when it rains. In college I would drive out
into the fields, down the empty highways, two lanes flagged
with fences, the cows ambling, the sun setting, the sky growing pink.
A secret: I let a man undress me because he wouldn't stop kissing me,
and though I found him to be beautiful, my mind moved to the light
shifting among trees in the evening, the fields unfolding.

Diorama (woman with rose-pattern tea set)

Walking through a great fire leaves you ruined but delicious.
Like fruit dunked quickly into boiling water,
your family is part of a recipe. After the day is assembled,
it will be baked and eaten, but by whom?

I've started noticing when it would be nice to burst into flames:
as I carry a loaded tray smoothly across the floor,
when I sit down on a sofa that matches my dress.

The shapes in the living room that had been my sisters
are especially bright. It doesn't matter that we come back every time.
We become fainter to one another.

When someone opens the front door without knocking.
When a button makes a little song as it falls down the stairs.
When I wipe a smudge from a pane of glass and a train stops whistling.

I'm not the only one keeping a list.
This is the sickness we'll eventually die from.

KATHERINE SHARPE
Noise

When Luce gets home, the girl is standing in her living room. She looks about thirty, raw and full of want.

"You must be Luce," the girl says, wheeling around. Jangling energy flies off her in every direction. She's been sent up from a magazine in the city. Luce has agreed the girl can stay here for the night, observe her, and interview her. The invitation is a favor from Luce to a man she is seeing. The man is much younger than Luce, a fling really, and the girl is some friend of his.

The girl wears jeans, sandals, and a black silk button-down with no sleeves. Her hair is wild with travel. She's not pretty or stylish, just young.

"Jon let me in," the girl says, blushing. "I hope that's OK. He said I could look around."

The girl stands on a Turkish rug whose edge is fraying. Behind her is the shelf of photos, art books, and souvenirs she was perusing before Luce came in. Oaxacan wood animals, Chardin and Basquiat, and an unframed snapshot taken in Greece, of Bennett, tan beneath a foolish sunhat, with Josephine, aged six, hanging from his arm like a monkey in the Mediterranean sun. Her swimsuit pulled down to reveal one flat, childish nipple.

Luce scans the room to see what else the girl has seen. Disorder. Dust on the sill. Stuffing showing through a split in the tufted French sofa she has meant to take to Valley Upholstery for repairs. A refrigerator with so much stuck-on paper it looks as if attacked by butterflies. Shopping lists, messages from Josephine's school. A pile of shoes by the door.

"You have great stuff," the girl says, shyly. "My place is basically all IKEA."

Luce waits a beat. *In person, Luce Holloway manipulates silence as skillfully as she does a bass guitar.* A different reporter wrote that, years ago. Dignifying Luce's lifelong grope for words. They were not the element her thoughts formed in; she was always translating. Still, the ridiculous statement held a grain. Luce had made delay work for her. It was part of her persona.

"Would you like a shower?" Luce asks. "I thought we'd go to dinner pretty soon."

"Oh, yes," the girl says. "Thank you."

Luce leads the girl through the house, up the steep servants' staircase of its elegant past, down the upper hall, past the suite she rents to Jon and his boyfriend, Neil. Reddish light spills out from beneath the closed door of the bedroom they sleep in, tinted by the mauve gauze curtains. From behind the door of Neil's painting studio comes a faint sound of radio.

Luce shows the girl where she will sleep, a small bedroom vacated recently by Josephine, who, upon turning fourteen, began to want a different, more commanding room at the front of the house. That one has windows overlooking the street, and though few people travel down this block, Luce feels the new room is both evidence and, somehow, a vehicle, of Josephine's increasing commerce with the outside world.

"This was Josephine's room," says Luce. "I'm sorry about the girl stuff everywhere." But it isn't really an apology, and Luce can see the girl greedily cataloging the details anyway, mentally adding them to her written piece.

> Luce Holloway, an icon of the avant-garde rock scene of the 1980s and '90s, newly divorced from her husband of thirty-two years, Bennett Lowe, lives in a rambling house in the Berkshires that she shares with two housemates, a Maine coon cat, and the detritus of her fast-growing daughter with Lowe, Josephine, who at fourteen has already graced the pages of Vogue…

Luce leaves the girl with a towel, sloppily folded but clean, and points out the bathroom. She goes downstairs. Standing at the sink, looking out the window, she fills the steel electric kettle with water. She taps chamomile tea out of a special tin. The tea was a gift from a road manager on her latest tour, in Germany. It is an Austrian blend: delicate little herbs from the Alps.

The kettle rushes. As Luce moves to lift it from the cradle, it occurs to her that the girl upstairs and the man she is seeing are sleeping together.

*

At six, Luce takes the girl to the third-nicest restaurant in town. They walk there, the town is small, the restaurant only half a mile away. Luce wears a top of sea-foam green with sculpted short sleeves that stand away from her arms like the suit of a samurai warrior, over slim white jeans and white leather ankle boots with the toes cut out. Her toenail polish is brick-colored, her blond and lacquered hair pulled into a loose knot. Luce wasn't born a beauty, just a tall tomboy. But she turned herself into one. At fifty-eight, it's been over ten years since she was first called "ageless" in the press.

At the corner of State Street a man in cargo shorts stares for a long moment. Luce observes him while pretending not to, in the way that has become habitual. Many people stare at her in the town. They know what she is, the star in their midst, even if they do not know exactly what her fame is for. Some must wonder where Bennett has gone, the tall man who went with her, with his T-shirt and spreading smile and mop of boyish, agitated hair. Others have no idea.

The girl, reinstated in her black silk top, trails Luce like a small storm cloud.

At the restaurant, Luce and the girl sit at a table with a white polyester cloth. A boy with razor burn brings them menus, his eyes brushing Luce's outfit, her face.

Luce looks around. She smells the hot and aggressive scent of butter on the edge of burning. Waiters and busboys float around the room, in black clothes and white half-aprons attached with binder clips at the waist. Beyond the plate glass windows it's still daytime. Luce's mind begins to wander, tracing the nubs of the obligations and favors that define her week. Without Bennett, she finds herself more vigilant. Review the schedule, review it again. Perhaps she should find some money for Jon, make him what he practically is already, a personal assistant. A second brain. She thinks she heard someone call a husband that once. Some time ago, when she had no thought of losing hers.

The girl sets down her menu softly, as if it might explode. She withdraws from her bag a small notebook, a pen, a smart phone, and a digital recorder. She places these items atop one another and straightens them. She has a meek, innocent look that scratches at Luce like grit.

"Before we begin," says the girl, and Luce has the sinking feeling that they will never, in fact, begin. "I want to talk about Evan." The girl lets the syllables hang in the air for a moment, the name of the man she and Luce evidently share. "It felt too strange not to mention it." She flicks a spare strand of glossy brown hair behind her ear. Her hair is her best feature.

Luce blinks slowly, producing a forbidding effect she's well aware of. "It's off the record," she says. "Way, way off the record, if that's what you mean. You're here to write the same article everyone writes."

"No, that's fine," the girl says. "I wanted to talk to you off the record."

The waiter brings Luce's salad, a plate of gloppy pasta for the girl.

"Are the two of you—?" asks Luce. She hates that she is curious, and does not want to have to say the words. Involved, fucking, an item. Whatever people say.

"No," the girl says. "Not anymore. We're just friends now." Her words are swift, and Luce believes her. She notes her own relief with irritation. What is it to her, what Evan does? What else Evan does.

"So what did you want to say?"

"Evan's not a bad guy," the girl begins, her statement pregnant with its own contradiction.

Luce waits. She is already sorry she agreed to this. She remembers the day Evan asked her if she would do this favor, would grant an interview to his dear friend, a super talented writer and a super big fan who could use it to break into a really great magazine. He had flattered Luce's longstanding habit of helping striving women. They'd been curled up together in the bed that Luce used to share with Bennett. She remembered feeling giddy, lightheaded. Evan was the first man she'd been with since Bennett, and he was just five years older than half her age. Everything about their connection had seemed surreal, from the moment he picked her up at an art opening near Little Italy, as smoothly and deftly as if she were some no-name girl. People often stared at Luce, but they rarely did what Evan had done, talked. The sun was streaming in the windows; the room was warm, the sheets and blankets on the bed churned into a choppy sea. At the beginning of their affair, Luce had felt constantly the way she had when married and waking up next to her husband from a dream of sex or flirtation with someone else, groggy and confused, both guilty and lit from within by a sense of the secret possibilities that hid inside the world.

The girl leans in, and her nose shines with oil. Evan isn't classically attractive either, but he has brio and charm. The girl is fanatical and beaten-down. She places a hand near each side of her head, as if trying to create a tunnel right between herself and Luce. "He's nice," she says, "and he's fun, up to a point. But he's not someone you can rely on." She stacks her words carefully, one on top of the next, building them up. "I wanted to warn you. You can't take him seriously."

The girl sits back. Luce again has a feeling that her life has become surreal, only instead of giddy and intoxicating, this time it is merely strange. Who is this girl? What is going on? Luce touches her own arm for reassurance.

"He's just a fling," says Luce. She wonders why she is defending herself. She'll be sixty; she is allowed to have a fling.

"That's what you think now," the girl says, bitterly.

"What is the problem?" Luce asks. "What exactly did he do to you?"

"He wasted my time," the girl whispers.

Luce does not know how to think about time. It would be too simple, and too sad, to say that someone has just wasted thirty-two years of hers, and yet this is a thing that could be said.

"We are not in the same position," says Luce.

"I know," says the girl, hangdog. "But you're Luce fucking Holloway! And believe me, you can do better than him." She stares down at her plate of congealing noodles. "It's too depressing to even live in a world where you can't do better."

Luce knows and doesn't like it, this talk of deserving. Other people have told her similar things, that Bennett didn't deserve her, or that Luce deserved better. How childish that outlook is, Luce thinks, that we should all get what we deserve.

"Evan's not important to me," says Luce.

"He will be."

"He broke your heart," Luce says.

The girl looks at her like a teacher or a coach about to give up on a pupil beyond helping. "Never mind," she says. "I said my thing. He's fun. Have fun. Maybe you're tired of famous people."

"This conversation's making me tired of everyone," says Luce. Somewhere on the internet there's a picture of her and Evan, taken by a social photographer on the red carpet of a fashion gala. He's wearing his one nice suit and she, a long cream-colored gown. In heels, she's taller than he is. She had been experimenting with taking him out in public. She remembers wondering whether Bennett would notice, whether he'd care.

The girl is looking past her now, scanning the seam where the walls meet the ceiling. Her mouth is set. Beneath her underarms there are darker crescents on her sleeveless silk shirt.

Luce squints at her. She knows this kind of girl, she thinks; she has read about them, girls today. They have sex with all the wrong people for a decade and feel that it's someone else's fault besides their own. They go around hollow-eyed and aggrieved. At forty, they write op-eds for *The New York Times*, wondering ingenuously whether it's too late to settle down. Her own daughter will never be like this. The very thought of Josephine brings Luce a cool flood of relief.

"Could we start?" says Luce. "You're running out of time for your interview." But it's all preamble with this girl, who launches into a speech about what Luce has meant to her, what her and Bennett's marriage meant, to the girl and to her entire generation. ("I mean," the girl says, "it's an overstatement, obviously, but you're kind of the reason I moved to New York.") Luce knows this maneuver; others have done it before, taking her life and curving it into some kind of meaning, as if she were responsible for a bunch of ordinary suburban girls who went to the city in search of some inchoate way of life, as if she were complicit, or had any of that in her head, ever. Luce thinks if she were twenty, twenty-five, she wouldn't be caught dead in New York. She'd go to Detroit, Berlin, somewhere else. She's read about a farm in Tennessee, a place full of kids who make punk music and sauerkraut. It sounded nice.

She waves her hand as if the words *New York* make her nauseous.

"People are upset, you know," says the girl. "About your breakup with Bennett. People are taking it really personally." She is too polite or stilted to say "divorce." "Nobody thought it could ever happen to you two."

"People don't have much imagination."

The facts of Luce's early life are well known. She married Bennett at twenty-four, after they'd already been playing music together for years. The band had its first gold record right before her twenty-ninth birthday. For a decade before that, they lived in Chicago. Bennett drove a truck for UPS and collected the works of obscure German industrial bands, which took effort, before the internet, when things could still be obscure. They practiced in the basement. Luce tried to paint for a while before giving that up in the wake of the band's success. In their early thirties they walked into New York like it was a conquered city. They'd been fixtures of the downtown scene ever since—till they moved north to raise Josephine.

Luce, of course, had her own baby old. She had been forty-three when Josephine was born. Bennett had always wanted a baby. Luce hadn't, or hadn't been sure, it's hard to remember. The pregnancy had been natural, an accident or nearly one. Quickly it felt right. Part of a tour was canceled. Luce remembered that time fondly, a brief lassitude after years of work. It had been a hot summer, the months when she was big. She'd received house calls from an acupuncturist in the daytimes, while Bennett was out recording a new side project. He'd come home sometimes to cook her what she wanted, big pots of soba noodles with Chinese greens, tofu, and peanut sauce. She'd felt regal. She had never regretted Josephine.

When Josephine was born, fashion-designer friends made the baby outlandish little garments out of scraps. Luce and Bennett raised her in a luxury so unlike their own upbringings. Luce's parents had been Christian Scientists. Josephine grew up with executives and rock stars. Luce created presence by channeling her own anxiety so that other people felt it, not her. Josephine appeared to be without discomfort. She had the brazenness: a purer power than Luce's, but also more common.

As the girl talks, Luce takes comfort in the thought of Josephine, her beauty and her lack of inhibition. They moved up north to try to give the girl a more ordinary life, to take her away from the world of money and fame that had been the only world she'd known, so it wouldn't warp her. The plan had not wholly succeeded. Instead of having other children of the famous to scrape against, to outflank her, Josephine here was without competition. She walked through life like a feudal queen, grabbing what she wanted. Luce knew she should try to stop her, but at some moments she felt proud, and at others, she didn't wish to admit that she didn't know how. Josephine had listened to Bennett—sometimes.

"May I share some reactions from social media?" asks the girl. She takes out scraps of paper and begins to read. Luce cuts her off.

"Is it hard?" She dandles her dinner knife while she talks, rolling the cutting end against the table.

"What?"

"Being alone. It's new for me." Luce surmises that the girl is alone. It's written all over her; she's like a sore.

"You're not alone," says the girl. "You're surrounded." Her eyes shine. She's picturing the house, with its enfolding circles of people, Jon, Neil, Josephine, all the books and the things and the chatter.

Luce knows that her life looks rich from the outside.

"I always had Bennett," says Luce. "Maybe I never—" She trails off.

"Luce!" The voice comes from behind her shoulder.

Luce turns. There's a woman approaching the table, short, mid-forties, striding with purpose in capri pants and a tunic woven through with metallic thread. She moves fast, as if she expects Luce to vanish or flee. Luce recognizes her; she is the head of the parent-teacher organization at Josephine's school.

"Luce. Did you get a call from Ms. Vanelli today?"

"No." Ms. Vanelli is the principal of Valley Middle.

"Really," says the woman, meaning if this is true, it's Luce's fault for being flighty and hard to reach.

Stephanie Mitchell—that's her name.

"I'm afraid your daughter and her friends are at it again."

Stephanie stands by the table and leans toward Luce, lowering her voice so the girl won't hear, though Luce suspects she hears everything. "It was my son," she says. "Whatever else Ms. Vanelli decides, I would like Josephine to call our home this weekend and apologize." She stands up, composes herself. "Pardon my intrusion, but you're not an easy person to get a hold of." Stephanie glares at the girl and Luce and back at the girl, then at the pile of recording devices on the table, as if to be interviewed is somehow indecent.

She walks away. Luce can see her make for a table where a man in a sport coat has his back turned, and a boy in shorts, who must be Josephine's age but looks like a child, with spindly white arms and legs, is stacking jars of mini mustard and knocking them down.

"What was that?" asks the girl.

Luce doesn't intend to answer but then she thinks, fuck it. They are still off the record. "You don't print anything about Josephine," she says.

"Of course not," says the girl.

"It's just this game," Luce says. "You know this age, how boys are smaller now. A bunch of girls at school have been taking boys, putting them in lockers."

"Lockers?"

"Yeah, you know. Humiliating them. Her son is one. She thinks that Josephine is a sort of leader."

The girl smiles shyly. So they are together on this, not minding the thought of boys in lockers.

"Josephine's having a hard year, of course, though she won't admit it," says Luce. "Bennett's girlfriend is closer to Josephine's age than mine and his. It's confusing." Privately she thinks, better beat up some boys than do those other things—cutting. The appalling things that girls are doing now. Luce knows she is supposed to be upset. Ashamed of Josephine's behavior and concerned about her future, not secretly half-wondering how long she can keep it going, steamrolling everyone who gets in her way. "Of course it's not all right," she says, waving insistently with her hand.

"No, I know," says the girl.

Over dessert Luce finds herself, to her own horror, really *talking*. She tells the girl things she hasn't spoken about yet. The house is going to hell. Old friends don't know how to treat her. Dating is a disaster, aside from Evan. It's so awkward, like middle school, but without the beautiful bodies and surging hormones. Like middle school on lithium.

The girl asks Luce if she wants to get married again.

"No," says Luce. "I want to be married to Bennett again."

"So it was good," the girl says.

"It was my life," says Luce. She sips her coffee. It's a coffee she ordered minutes ago, then called the waiter back to fortify with brandy. The warm burn reminds her of winter in Chicago, which in turn reminds her of winters in North Dakota, growing up. She gets nostalgic. "At fourteen," she says, "I was running through wheat fields. I was reading. I didn't know about anything."

"You grew up fast," says the girl.

"Well, yes," says Luce, "I grew up. I didn't get stuck in adolescence, like people now."

*

Luce and the girl walk back to the house. In the kitchen, Neil stirs a pot of pasta on the stove. His glasses when he looks up are opaque with steam. Jon sits beside the wooden table piled with newspapers, his feet up in bright argyle socks. His dreadlocks are beautiful, puffy and loose, extending behind his head. He's got a large book of some kind of Renaissance art propped on the table. He's studying it closely. Sometimes he pauses to point something out to Neil: a lovely sky, an especially good *putto*.

"Glass of wine?" says Jon. The girl looks at Luce as if seeking permission.

"OK," she says for herself. "Thanks."

"Where's Josephine?" asks Luce. "Has she called?"

"Oh, Josephine," says Neil, stirring the pasta with a mournful air. "*Jo-jo-jo-JO-jo-jo-jo,*" he sings, an arpeggio.

"Said she was going to a party at Wilshire College," says Jon.

"Then she said she was joking," Neil adds.

"Was she joking?" asks Luce.

"Who knows with her."

"Said she was going to Clive's to study math," says Jon.

"Would you call Clive's mom?"

"Would you like me to?"

"Thanks."

Luce walks off to her wing of the house to put on something more comfortable.

After she changes, Luce takes the girl to the TV room. She plays some footage the girl has asked to see: old VHS videos of herself in a short skirt, on stage in Asia. Climbing all over an amp. Luce remembers this show. It was before Josephine. She and Bennett had been arguing about something that afternoon. She recalls making up later, reaching for him in a hotel room's muggy dark.

"Wow," the girl says. "This is phenomenal."

On stage, Luce jumps off the amp, then lies down and grinds erotically underneath her bass. It's been a long time since she watched a performance from this far back. The image is poor quality, hectic with hot spots and shadow, but it reveals a likeness of herself to Josephine that Luce has never noticed before. There on camera are her daughter's long, muscular limbs, her lank blond hair and upward-tilted face.

In the TV room, Luce touches her face with the cool back of her hand. She's always taken pride in her stage act. Athletic and confrontational, much dissected by fans and critics, it is the achievement that feels most her own, even more than the music. But she's unsettled by the vision of Josephine up there, writhing and throwing herself around carelessly like a doll.

On video, the figure in the short skirt collapses to the stage, wailing and pounding the ground with its fists. Nearby, Bennett and the rest of the band loom and spin, grating intently at the necks of their guitars. Sound pours from the stadium speakers, layers of distortion, mazelike and heavy. "Noise," the music press called them, first derisively, then as a term of description and even praise, when it came to hail them as pioneers of a new genre: noise music, or noise rock.

Luce shifts in her seat. She wishes she could run out onto the stage, throw a blanket over her younger self, guide her off somewhere dim and safe. She doesn't know what she's doing, Luce thinks, and the thought reverberates unpleasantly. Despite her heavy investment in the appearance of confidence, has Luce ever really known what she was doing?

She aims the remote at the set, jabbing with her thumb to bring the volume way down. The girl sighs a little; light from the TV gilds the edge of her face.

"What really happened with you and Bennett?"

"He'd been cheating for years," says Luce. "I knew and I didn't know." She had never called him out on it. It was never the activity she would have preferred, tearing it all open, rending the ground she lived on. "We fought a lot. It's not part of his public personality, but we did. Finally, as you know, he met someone he wanted to be with more."

The girl is silent, her head down, twisting the fringe of the throw blanket around her fingers. She turns to Luce and nods slowly. Her meaning sinks in more fully this time: she is inviting Luce to agree that the two of them are the same in this way, women who've made do, always, with too little. For a second Luce thinks she is about to reach forward, place a consoling hand on her arm. She stiffens. *We are not in the same position*, she would like to say again—but the girl hasn't spoken, so there's nothing to refute.

It's so unfair that men matter, she thinks. She tries not to picture Bennett now, reaching for another, younger body. She tries not to know all the reasons Evan isn't equivalent, why dating him does not mean keeping pace with Bennett in the furtive race to do better and not be the one left behind. She doesn't want Evan, not drivingly, not down in her soul. She wants to be onstage with Bennett. She wants, even more, to be in the backyard at some time in the past, grilling weenies, feeling thong sandals between her toes, watching Josephine and Bennett play-fight, knowing that he'll walk over soon and put his arm around her.

Luce dips her head back against the sofa. In her room earlier, she took a Xanax, and now she lets it tow her under. She wakes up with her mouth lolling open. The room is dark. The girl is gone, the TV's playing snow, and her shoulders are freezing where the blanket has slipped off. She gets up and makes her way down the hall to her large room. As she passes the head of the stairs, she hears a burst of laughter from the kitchen: the girl's high voice, mixing with her two housemates' masculine ones. She pads to her door and stands for a while with her hand on the knob.

The next day is Saturday. Luce is up early. Josephine sleeps late, her door closed. Jon says he saw her come in. When Luce asks him how she was, he says, "Oh, the usual—sullen inscrutable." Luce takes the girl to Stop & Shop for groceries, then sends her to town to have lunch. She means to do some work; she is introducing a film at a festival in New York on Friday. She is supposed to meet Evan for dinner after, but she no longer wants to. She feels a time of quietness coming. The knowledge comes in images, a hand muffling the mouth of a bottle. She wants to text him but can't summon the words. She just won't show up at dinner. He'll know.

The girl comes back. She looks refreshed, potentially fortified.

"I drank too much last night," she confides. "I stayed up a bit with Jon and Neil."

"Oh?" says Luce.

"Yeah," says the girl. "They're…inspiring."

"I'm glad," says Luce. "Cup of tea before you go?" The girl is due in Springfield to catch a train at one-thirty. Jon will drive her.

"Sure," says the girl. Luce makes the tea and takes it out to the yard. The yard alone is enough to make this place great, an oval clearing ringed by trees, behind the house, with a view to a levee and some blue mountains beyond. Luce and the girl sit in front of the picnic table, on the same bench, looking out.

Luce blows on her tea. "I don't want you to write about us," she says. She woke up this morning feeling a little better, as though she'd regained something during the night.

The girl stares down through the green depths of her tea. "That's not fair," she says. Luce sips from her mug. Two small white butterflies tumble through the air. "I'll let you read it first," says the girl. "I'll let you approve of everything."

"I'm sorry," says Luce.

"This was going to be a big deal for me," says the girl.

"I know."

"I could write it anyway."

"I know a lot of people," says Luce. "I could make it hard for you to write about music again."

"Bullshit," says the girl, but she keeps the same defeated slump in her shoulders.

Luce looks out through the trees. There's mildew on the hammock.

"Why?" says the girl. "You have to at least tell me why."

"I really don't," says Luce.

Will Evan tell the girl that Luce dumped him? Will the girl think it has something to do with her foolish warning? They can have each other, Luce thinks. They can all have each other.

The side door squeaks; the plastic seam that runs along the edge is frayed and sagging. Josephine comes out. She whams the door shut behind her, which is what you have to do to get it closed.

"Mom," she says, a one-word bleat that is both complaint and salutation. Josephine greets the world, this year, by finding it lacking. It's how she connects.

Josephine walks into the yard, switching back and forth on her long colt legs. She's wearing shorts Luce doesn't like, shorts so skimpy they reveal the transition point from thigh to bottom. Luce doesn't criticize them; she is in no position to, with all the things she's worn. She lets Jon do the teasing. So far, Josephine's showed a disinclination to be shamed. When Jon says she looks like a street-walker, Josephine shakes it.

Now she steps over to the hammock and flops into it, like an exquisite fish netting itself. Watching her daughter gives Luce a pang of pain and pleasure. She is beautiful and tall, like her famous mom and dad. See? Luce wants to say to the girl. See this magnificent daughter? This is the kind of people we are. We are like ourselves, not you. Josephine surfaces again, hauling herself up to sit on the hammock cross-legged.

"Jon says you were out till midnight last night," says Luce.

"Yep," says Josephine.

"So you said ten."

"Sorry," says Josephine, in an un-sorry tone.

"What were you studying?"

"Math," says Josephine, dreamily. She's holding a cell phone in a pink plastic case.

"You need to tell Jon or me or someone when you're running late, OK?"

"Fine, I will," says Josephine, in a condescending tone, as if her mother is being unreasonable here.

Luce feels flattened, out of the will to fight. She already knows she won't say anything about Stephanie Mitchell. Josephine, Josephine, Josephine. Luce misses Bennett so sharply right now. He was the more gifted parent. Even when Josephine was a baby, he had an easier time suspending himself and becoming the receptive blankness that a child needs. Her childhood is over now. Luce will consider boarding school in the fall. Some other local musician's kid goes to a good one, she's heard, in Pennsylvania. Luce will ask. It would not be a cruelty. Josephine would love to be among plutocratic children. She needs a whetstone to sharpen herself against. Still, Luce feels a sense of failure, of loss. So it ends like this, the needle slipping off the record, not one great big final swell.

Josephine raises the phone to sternum level and adjusts her legs underneath herself in the hammock. Soon there is almost no sound at all in the yard, just the occasional rustle of a squirrel in the trees, and the soft thud of Josephine's thumbs against the screen of her device, which she works with such commanding intensity over there that Luce thinks she could be administering a small republic.

Down the bench, the reporter sits in her creased silk shirt from yesterday. She has swept her hair to one side, exposing the pale curve of her neck. Now that she's leaving, Luce feels sorry for her. She'd like to get her attention, make at least some gesture of apology. She makes a half-turn toward her and waits to be noticed, but the girl purses her lips and tilts her head away.

All right, Luce thinks. That's fair.

The reporter goes back to watching Josephine, so Luce does too—at first to play off the snub, but then with gathering attention. In the hammock, the child bends prayerfully over her phone. Luce leans forward; her throat is stiff. She feels tensely alert, like a scientist hoping to glimpse a phenomenon both brief and highly specific, and she is aware that the reporter to her side has dropped into a similar posture. We're waiting for something, she thinks. Both women are staring now, but Josephine makes no protest. Luce can tell she doesn't see them anyway, just the bright screen that pours her outward, into the world.

Mare

There is no law against evil. You buried your son alone
under a lime tree. He was almost a boy

but they called him something else, as though
you had carried him up a staircase inside you

and missed a step. I never knew you with long hair,
without your thick history. The light held your face

like a chisel. God was a clock hanging above us
working his gold hands backward. You spoke of heaven

as though you had been there and found it
wanting. There were whole forests

you made just to lose me in—you knew I would always
come home. There is no law against evil.

So I learned to gather the night rain
in the place a soul should be. I never ate

at that table in your mind where the other children sit,
each small head bent and blank with thanks.

AURELIE SHEEHAN
Buck's Bar

The sign is nailed to a two-by-four, part of a raw wood skeleton built around the door. In the last few minutes the snow has brightened, and the barbed wire fencing and the trees on the horizon scrawl out messages—mainly that any notions I might've had are wrong here. I walk past a dog in the bed of a blue Chevy. I've never been to a bar in a trailer before.

One woman stands by a bottle of cinnamon whiskey. Others, in red, white, and blue bikinis, stand or squat by cars, motorcycles, ATVs, and bottles of beer. The pool table is Christmas bright, a more ethereal blue coming from behind a row of liquor. The bartender looks at me, as do six men on stools who've twisted their bodies to stare.

Another resident told me she goes to the bars and just nurses one bottle all night. Cold sober, she scrawls notes in the bathroom. But I'm not here to report on anything or observe.

"Is Scotty here?"

The bartender is my father's age. He's not fully listening. He's a gray blur turning away as I wait, hands on the bar.

"Scotty?" I think I hear him say.

The two men closest to me are wearing hunting, not ranching, gear. It's different. You're allowed a bright color or two for ranching, because the animals already know you're there. I eat meat; I'm not against ranching. Least of all ranching in this state, where the cows seem to have a fairly decent life. That is, until slaughter.

If I say what I think, I'll eventually have no friends. If I say what I think, it'll be like whittling a stick to a point or still further.

One of the men takes kindly to me. "Scotty took off ten, twenty minutes back."

"OK. Shit."

The men come in two types. Long and wiry, economically built, like a coyote. Or the balloon men. This one is a coyote.

"Take a load off. He'll be back soon."

"I can't. There's a problem."

"What's your problem, little missy?" asks the man next to him, leaning forward.

I'm crawling on my hands and knees. Fine tall daisies and black-eyed Susans bend and separate under my palms. I know it must hurt but I don't feel it hurting. Grasses swish on my hips and tickle my feet. The sun is a storm. I feel the proximity of shade, know that shade is possible. It's just a game I'm playing here.

Let's start with Mac Gilgamesh. A composite of all the boyfriends I've ever had. That I think this is probably disadvantageous for him. And yet, I do believe, he is new and rare. And this, too, is probably disadvantageous for him.

It was a big surprise to even *have* a boyfriend. I hadn't gotten over the surprise of that.

We met at a work function. Toward the end of the event, we were both standing at the buffet, sliding bagels into our bags: options for lunch or dinner.

"Isn't that—the legend of Gilgamesh?" I said, looking at his nametag.

"Indeed," he said. "It's my legend and I'll cry if I want to."

He stared soullessly at me. He was slim and had sad posture. His black shirt was so old it had turned blue, shiny along the edges, as if he'd been dipped in silver.

I wondered how much food was in his bike messenger bag.

We sat outside on a wall and talked and watched people.

"I'm a writer, I guess," I said. At times, my day job as a proofreader dampened conviction. Or at least made me feel like I didn't have the right to say things.

He threw a bit of bagel to a pigeon. "I'm a writer too."

He laughed half-heartedly. Maybe the planet was filled with writers. Maybe the coincidence of being writers was a cliché at this point.

We talked about the kind of writing we did—he was sci-fi and I was, well, defined poorly. He told me about a trip he'd taken with his parents the year before. They'd hiked across Britain, picnicking on the steps of churches and peeing in fields. They spoke to a bunch of old chaps and innkeepers. It was the oldest trail in the country.

He was big on calling neighborhoods by their names. For instance, he lived in Murray Hill. I liked the way he said that. It made me think of those phone exchanges that used letters as well as numbers, and matchbooks with lovers' numbers written inside, and martinis and Manhattans. He made me feel connected to New York, though I'd only lived in the city a year.

One weekend, we went to the beach town in New Jersey where Mac used to go as a kid. We had to rent a car, which was expensive. Anything over two digits was expensive for us (sometimes anything over one digit). He paid with a credit card. It felt like bad luck to use the card without hope of paying it back anytime soon. Mac waited at the counter stoically, with a for-me but without-me determination. I asked about splitting the bill. I probably didn't ask hard enough.

At the house, Mac stood out on the screened-in porch in the cold. It was mid-afternoon but already felt like the sun was going down. I could see him through the door to the kitchen. He stood there for a long time.

We had sandwiches on the beach, and a bottle of wine. We drank from plastic cups decorated with holly that we'd found in the cabinet. The wine tasted great and so did the food. There's nothing like a roast beef sandwich with tomato and creamy horseradish relish and red wine on a freezing beach. We had potato chips also. The ocean didn't look like any water I'd ever seen. It might have said one thing to one person, but it said another thing to me.

After we ate the sandwiches, we nestled closer and rearranged the musty old sleeping bag, folding it over our legs. The wine bottle toppled and we had to grab for it. The red in the sand looked scary and Elizabethan, and then it settled down and became a skeleton key.

Mac didn't like to get drunk. He was careful with his consciousness, as if it were a bird's nest in need of tending. That meant I could get drunk alone, pretend to stay sober but be drunk alone, or stay sober. Ish.

Equations can keep you company, but they can also build tiny chain-link fences, like a crown.

An entire family—cousins, grandparents, a bunch of kids—trudged toward us on the shore. The women wore saris: tangerine, red and white, emerald. I had to blink to take in all the color. The children were playing a marching game.

That night in the Gilgamesh family friends' bed, I experienced an orgasm better than any I'd ever had, courtesy of another human being.

I felt like crying, but no tears came.

In the first days of my residency at the foundation, I sat in the kitchen with Sheila. It was riveting to watch her chop tomatoes. She hacked at them in the can, like an act of murder, before slowly leveling them into a pot crackling with garlic in olive oil. It was rumored she'd been to prison. She was thin and had some health problems—that was also a rumor. As the foundation chef, she existed in a space constructed of speculation. I sat at the counter and tried to un-know what I didn't know, and not to crush on her too terribly.

"So, you grew up in Wyoming?"

"Yup, mostly. I moved here from the Dakotas when I was a kid." She began chopping the first of two green peppers.

"What was it like?"

"What was what like? My life? My childhood?" She gave me a look. She had a long braid and a high forehead.

"That's a broad question, isn't it?"

"It was good, a good childhood." She turned back to the cutting board. "Next question? Or how about this: what was *your* childhood like, Aurelie?" The pepper pile was resplendent and bright green. Her fingers were long and competent, and everything was mixed up for a moment. I didn't know who I was or why I was there. I blinked. She was still slashing, her back straight and sturdy.

The station wagon's steering was so loose I had to keep both hands on the wheel. I'd quit so-called work for the day with the idea I'd drive to town, thirty miles away, to pick up a few things at Walmart. In that landscape, with houses far from the road and from each other, night locks in as an alternate, maybe dangerous dimension. Dusk was descending and I was living a dream. In my Paris-bought gang boots and my fashion-forward tartan shirt, I'd convinced myself that I wasn't just a dandelion head or a butterfly hairclip; maybe I could really *do* this thing.

There were only three radio stations to choose from: Christian, "yesterday's" rock, and country. No Patsy Cline or Johnny Cash, so I'd settled on "Sweet Home Alabama." I'd turned it up, and I was getting back into those years when I didn't know anything, my Connecticut years, and it was fun to barrel down the empty road in the near dark, luminescent fields on either side—grasses blanched in the rising moonlight, snow patches from a spit storm an hour past—and barbed wire fences everywhere, did I tell you that? Barbed wire went on for miles and miles, in slackness and sharpness, and once in a while you'd see a turnoff with a cattle guard, or you'd rumble over a piece of road kill—but knowing what you know doesn't help when the time comes, because knowing is like being. It doesn't last. It's a lie. It becomes an illusion when the next thing comes. And the next thing, in the blackness, was that a deer leapt in front of the station wagon. I saw it in my peripheral vision, tan-white against the gray-black of sixty miles an hour. Head high, front legs extended, body an octagon, a tender delicate bag, a home with a hearth, and I didn't see the back legs at all, didn't even have time to brake until the animal had been hit, until I hit the animal is how it needs to be said, and then the deer disappeared. It was as if, with my dumbass Yankee ways, my dumbass Sweet Home Alabama ways, my dumbass fake-ass ways, I entered a different dimension, a place where change happens, where deer disappear. That deer just fucking disappeared. Then I saw what I thought was my deer—I called him my deer—running. A shape on the other side of the road. But he didn't get through the fence. He jumped the fence. He tried to jump the fence. Instead of getting over the fence he got into the fence, somehow. A deer, half dead from my car, was now stuck in the barbed wire fence on a state highway in Wyoming, and night slammed down like a door.

When Mac lay on his back, his hips and ribs jutted up against his skin. His face was regal, like a young King Lear. Didn't anyone realize that all kings were princes once, and even before that they were little fawns?

He ventured: "I wish you'd stay at my place sometimes."

"Don't say that. You know how I am about the loft bed."

"I know, it's just sometimes—I like the idea of sharing *my* life."

My head buzzed and my mouth went dry. I had to say something. "We should hang out there for dinner sometimes. Or rent movies."

Mac nodded and smiled, with caution and panic. It was the world championship of shy suffering.

The day before I left, we walked through Central Park. The sky was a fragile airy bronze, with hues of pink and blue.

He was brave and generous in the face of the news, this pesky little being-two-thousand-miles-away thing. We walked the fat paths. He held my hand firmly, as if we were going over a chancy bridge. He looked ahead. It was only temporary!

The shiny black origami of whatever it was, the darkness, hadn't gone away with Mac—but I'd been able to keep it at arm's length. We'd been able to console each other. *Still would, still would, still would.* The miles would mean nothing to me.

Scotty was the one who picked me up at the airport, swinging my suitcase into the bed of his pickup with shotput ease. His black dog looked at me neutrally. "Good deal," Scotty said, when I said just about anything. He dropped me off at a geodesic dome half a mile down a dirt road and gave me the station wagon keys.

I began to call it home and it was a kind of home, this anomalous outpost, blue-green carpeting everywhere, including the bathroom. The interior walls were flat and understandable, but the dome itself was made with radical timber, cut and nailed into geometric shapes, like the innards of an umbrella. I saw the other residents at weekday dinners, or at special events, or as we crossed paths at the office. Later, at bars.

Nights started early in that dome house, and as I lay in bed, miles from anyone, I thought about how any screams would go unanswered. But fear is hard to sustain, and I achieved an unlikely sangfroid.

I bought a book on conversational French and sat in the sunroom and attempted to learn verb construction. (I suppose I could have been writing.) Out the window, the hills were neverending and they were so shapely, cut-outs without any blur, and I wanted to walk the edge where earth met sky, with a picnic basket or a shotgun, depending on which way I wanted to take all this. I slipped on my Parisian motorcycle boots and explored. I took up smoking again. I drank bourbon.

My dreams didn't seem to have anything to do with my life, with who I was or had become or was becoming. But they laid down their own law, succinct dramas where no one was winning.

I became supernatural, or at least superstitious. Sometimes I'd open the door and stand on my doorstep and try to take it all in. Out of the blackness, the shuddering of a black cow in the adjacent field. Out of the blackness, the screech of a prehistoric bird or a wolverine. Some nights, the moon was so bright the hills looked like daytime. Or the dark became extreme, so solid that it felt like a bloated demon had taken over the entire world and would swallow me too.

I know I can't expect Wyoming to conform to my Eastern ways, but I still feel a prickle at the back of my neck, optimism maybe, telling Len and Rick what happened.

"So where was this?" Rick asks, looking into my eyes with new focus.

"Just down the road. And I was looking for Scotty to help me get him off the fence. Could you help me?"

They're on their feet. As Len quizzes me further on where we're going, Rick talks to the men at the bar. They laugh, and then Rick joins Len and me and we head outside.

"You want to follow me, then?" I ask. The dog is still watching.

I pull out and back onto the state highway. I stay under the speed limit, as if I've got cops, not cowboys, behind me. I go a little faster. The road is straight and the land is gray and white, sketched with the wire and broken trees, but these fragments or dreams blur into darkness. I begin to panic that I won't see the deer, that I've already passed him. Len and Rick look like Mafiosos now, gangsters in my rearview.

Then there is a shape on the fence and I brake. The deer isn't quite hanging, but he's held in place. He twists in my headlights, neck and head extending up and away, leg treading the air. I get out of the car and call senselessly, "It's OK, it's OK," and Len is shouting at me from back by their truck. "Miss, please. Do not disturb the animal." I stare back at them—they've pulled over and Rick is doing something behind the door. I start walking in their direction, away from the deer, but now Len and Rick are approaching me rapidly. Rick is holding a gun.

"Hold on," I yell into the cold dark. "What's the gun for?"

Len puts a hand on my shoulder. "Miss, don't worry. First, we'll see if we can help him get out safely. Likely we'll need to shoot him, Miss. For his own sake."

*

The man who took naked pictures of me was tall as Mac, but his tallness and thinness had a kind of unimpeachable European austerity built in. The times I saw him around the compound, he was walking with his hands linked behind his back, contemplating stalks of wheat. He had a very small camera, which seemed like a virtue, artistically speaking. He was older than any of the other residents.

Before one group dinner, he leveled his gaze at me, thorny eyebrows a-swirl, greyhound face trained in my direction. Would I be willing to model for a project? It was no problem at all if I didn't want to, he'd completely understand. Not my face, mind you. Only my body would be visible. I'd lie under heavy-looking objects. Apparently, he'd been making these objects for weeks, using Styrofoam, spray paint, and balsa wood. A far cry from wheat stalks, I thought. He was planning on using a few bodies. So for the female body, would I—perhaps?

"Um," was my initial response, a way station between alarm and acceptance.

His pants were some Old World version of trousers, not athletic gear, but not jeans either. He wore a fanny pack, for god's sake.

Back in the geodesic dome that night, I looked at myself in the mirror. I thought about Mac, who averted his eyes when I got dressed. After our vivid intimacies, our panting reliance on one another's hands and tongues and instruments and openings, he felt the need for discretion. He was the most respectful lover I'd ever encountered. Pleasure and then distance: perfect for someone like me. Privacy was a virtue: a thought I didn't have so much as kept realizing.

Sundays were quiet, in that the residents didn't meet for dinner, and the highway running through the property had less traffic than usual (one truck per hour instead of two). It was a couple of weeks after the spaghetti-making spectacle of Sheila and Aurelie-esque non-intimacy. I was with another resident, also from New York, taking a late afternoon walk. As we passed the meetinghouse, we saw Sheila in the driveway, arguing with a woman we didn't recognize. We kept walking, but slowly—we were tourists, rubberneckers, trying to look and not look. There was a commotion, maybe a thump, definitely a wail. The other woman had taken hold of Sheila's braid and slammed her head into the truck door. Sheila bounced out of her grip and away from the truck, and the two women were screaming at each other, then they both got into their separate trucks, and, high-school rebel style, peeled out of the driveway.

The next afternoon, Sheila was in the kitchen trussing up roast chickens. I said hi. She said hi. I said, "I actually meant to say—I saw you yesterday, with that woman. She—"

"You mean the daughter of the owner of this place? You saw us? What did you think?"

"I thought—"

The house was warm and the walls were dark red and all the appliances gleamed. I could hear the clock ticking. Sheila looked open for the first time, vulnerable, loving, beautiful, like we could talk, like she would tell me all about being in prison and I could be a help to her, a companion, and—

"When you finish thinking let me know. Dinner's at seven," She turned back to the chickens. Except for the one chicken who walked away.

We poured whiskey into tin coffee cups, a hint of the country. He arranged lenses on the counter and I sat on a stool and drank. A light stand was already set up when I got there. He asked me to lie under the wood and Styrofoam structure, dressed, performing an advance-version of myself. He flicked on the light, adjusted the angle and intensity.

When the time came, I undressed, putting my pants, shirt, underpants, and socks on the stool, as if I were prepping for a medical procedure. I stood straight, aligned with the Styrofoam. He said, loosen up your arms, your shoulders. The next sequence was of me holding the large cube, then lying underneath it. It wasn't heavy, but I did feel a little claustrophobic. I tried not to show this in my body.

It was a surprise when he undressed also, ducking out of his Euro pants, flinging his old-guy T-shirt, and came into the picture too, facing the structure and closing his eyes as the automatic shutter released.

"Thanks. This is really great," he murmured at the end, leveling a slow, velvety gaze in my direction, then starting to pack up. I tossed back the rest of my whiskey and drove to the geodesic dome. The night was cold, stars everywhere, and the sky a little dense also with the tallest cottonwoods you've ever seen.

I was writing a story about France, and so there was a reason for, you know, learning how to conjugate, and I stared at French fashion websites too. I had the sense that you could learn things from osmosis, from listening and looking and feeling. My mornings in Wyoming were spent in Verdun, and then in the afternoons, I staggered out of the dome house into the fields, and it became unnerving: reality. I had to concentrate to remember Mac, our connection, to conceive of a world where we were together.

The day after the shoot, a rattlesnake lay on my front step. I screamed, but then I saw that it wasn't moving. In fact, it was hollowed out, flat as a flying squirrel, head smashed. How could I have mistaken this for danger? The deadness was obvious. Had someone brought it to me? Had a hawk dropped it? But this cut all the way down the body—it seemed, for the wild, unnecessary.

I called Mac, though I knew he was still at work.

"I love you," he said.

"I love you too," I said.

Or did I say "I love you" first and then he said "I love you too"? As soon as I got off the phone, I wasn't sure.

Love was something we'd agreed upon. We'd seen good in each other and we both wanted to be brave and feeling. We used words, getting used to them, rolling them around our mouths like nonsense sounds, a foreign language, and each time we said them we linked closer, as if we'd cut strips from construction paper and taped the colorful loops around our wrists, and then to one another.

It was after Sheila and before Philip that I got the idea for a Christmas present for Mac, a way to make everything work for everybody.

I went to the rope store. A rope store doesn't just sell rope—they also sell hats, saddles, all kinds of cowboy gear. I started with the Wranglers. Mac's body type was perfect for Wranglers. I spent a long time sifting through rodeo shirts. Pearlized buttons and snapping cuffs, fanciful stitching, contrasting yokes. I selected one with a green and black Navajo-inspired pattern and this *piece de resistance* embroidered buffalo on the back. Then I turned to the belt buckles. "Does your boy compete?" asked the giraffe-like clerk when I laid down my credit card.

"What?"

"In the rodeo," she said, but by then she'd given up on me.

If the moon was low or gone or out or wherever moons go, the bedroom in my geodesic dome was dark as—so dark you could see things that weren't there.

The morning I left New York, Mac came by with pastries and coffee. I blinked down into the bag of gargantuan chocolate-chip muffins. Could not even think about eating. The existence of my subletter felt like a weather system that wouldn't go away. Someone was going to live in my apartment. She was going to trail her fingers over my things.

A strong sense of anti-purpose swamped me. I felt overwhelmingly grateful for Mac, his black-clad self, and, underneath the faded clothes, his white skin, decorated with paisley whorls of black, two hundred fake mustaches on a lean, scanty body. I started laughing. I felt emotion, didn't know *what* emotion, but as if someone had wrapped my belly with a belt and squeezed.

But I wasn't meant for love—for Mac Gilgamesh—or so I thought or so I knew—as the plane hovered, wanting to go, wanting, wanting, and then there was the push of it, the sheer volume of intent, forward, up, so unlikely, hundreds of tons of steel and then all these squishy centers—*I wasn't meant for love*—and so I could and would take on this adventure, up into the skies and down again. I'd sworn to Mac nothing would change, not a single stitch of anything, and I assured myself of the same. But then these words, in the plane. As if I were playing a role: the role of the adventurer, a lone someone.

I had been alone all my life—that's the way it felt. But this would be a different kind of alone. It would highlight the fact. Alone with cowboys and open spaces and terror and lightning. It was really going to be a question of reinvention. How long do you hold the egg in colored water to make a pretty pattern?

*

Len and Rick walk ahead of me. Rick lifts his gun and cocks his head, and, pointing the gun at something, something I'm supposed to pay attention to, to notice, to do something about, he shoots. The deer no longer struggles in the barbed wire. His head hangs. The wire sags with his weight. Len and Rick giant-step into the snow bank. Together they work to remove the deer from the wire, and they drag the carcass by its front legs to the side of the road. Len passes me on his way to the truck. He says it's better this way. I walk over to where Rick is standing and the deer is lying. We look down together. It is not a boy deer, as I'd thought. It's a girl deer. That's what I get from Rick, who says, "Girl wouldn't have made it. At least now someone can have a meal."

COURTNEY FAYE TAYLOR
Light flyweight

I do a summer job,
flaunting the *"Round 2"* sign
for the ring. I never wear thongs
or wink. The boys swing at musk air
all butterfly, but where the hell's that
exalted bee?   All July, police play games
involving pepperspray against boys with frigid
fathers   but in this ring, no boy
is born of any man who wintered him.   One suffers
uppercuts, works a warm yellow in
the loser's briefs. Another sprains ankles and
sometimes eats his water hard to be
more a feather. My half brother knocks me
into a pool all clothed 'cause I nickname him
MuNappy Ali.   My joke makes his penis
jump but he hates being likened to *the nigga
with Parkinson's*–paralysis reminds him
of joints, then "joint" reminds him of custody.   I wonder, does
an opponent's red glove seem like
a stoplight benighted when it speeds
at his coral lip? Is carpal bossing ever
caused by a need to be whooped
instead of whooping? When my boys
aren't turning white boys
turquoise they drive Coke trucks to
keep the gas and living
daylights on. Once I get my license I'll peer up
for sweaty flashes of them on boulevards, but
nothing. Real Truckers are blond mops, blue
sights, unfrisked, paid
well– you know that.   The open road is a bunch
but it's not that juvenile craft of rope caging a mat,

or the smell of Funyun breath knocked out of
one boy and jabbing towards the famine
of another.

COURTNEY FAYE TAYLOR

Blooms exactly

after Larry Levis

My youth?   I spent it all between
the knees of hairbraiders, begging kanekalon
to name me a debutante or mistake me
foreign. Those knees I matured between

worked weeks at *Kween of Kinks*

Braid Boutique, which was an old U.S. Cellular, behind
which my boyfriend's Chevrolet vanished under sleet. And
southern magnolias in hibernation pulsed like sea channels, or
seemed to channel, a yearly seedy casualty all over. I cleaned

for the braiders on Fridays. They sprawled

their slippered feet on the shampoo bowls whenever I
brought the vacuum around and hummed my 2010 urbanite
tunes: *Bedrock, Bottoms Up, No Hands*—sexist verses I saved
for the bathroom while lemon-scenting the shitter and

spritzing some Chanel No. down my bloomers, blooming
where you know it blooms exactly. Still even when
I smelled good, I smelled busy. And I hated high school.
Novembers I rode the 60 to Wauwatosa Mall just to sniff

the food court's teriyaki and auntie sugar pretzels. Those
bus rides were so boring that I pretended to smoke candy
canes, clicking an inkpen in front of the sucked pointy end to
imitate igniting. Sometimes boys with flies undone

      jittered past me towards the Rosa seats
      without my noticing. And from my window

I watched trashcans of all purposes blow their hearts out
across crosswalks. I had a knack for telling city garbage
from residential garbage: Tampons, Crown Royal, tattered Crisis mags
   or   playbills for *Fences*, gold minute hand of a wristwatch,

jaybird bones.   So why not admit it? I was petrified
then. My boyfriend drove past Decorah where the boy scouts
camped. His Chevy must've seemed Xzibit-pimped to the fist-
headed campers whose kickballs and cameraphones too
often sought the hood. Their curiosity left no dent, but say

it had; no boy would pay. This hood wasn't their hood
to heal. Hella girls at my high school from hoods unhealed

aced parabolas, sailed me by to ivies and housewifery.
All night they enthralled my jealousies with nothing on
but the height of their nipples.   Mine, Eiffel-tall
in my father's chilly condo, which stayed chilly so that

my hardness gave a show as I lazed
towards the kitchen in a camisole for some Minute
Maid. Had I known what my upper half
was making this man do for temperature

                I would've laughed.   I was a damn good merry maid.

Bleach licks. Pocketed fro picks. Egregious tips. A life
like that?   It seemed to kill me forever.

DIANA SPECHLER
An Older Woman

She had a bed that came out of her wall. Every night, she made it appear and every morning, she made it disappear. "I never knew anyone like you," he told her the first time he watched the magic trick.

"What, a grown woman with a murphy bed? You think when I was your age I imagined I'd have a murphy bed? Don't stay in this city forever. This city will make you forty-two years old with a murphy bed and a thirty-year-old lover."

"That sounds nice," he said.

She had a bathtub that stood on porcelain paws. "Do you ever go in it?" he asked her.

"Honestly, never. That's the New York way. You never go to the art museums. You never eat at your neighborhood bistro. You definitely never take a bath in your own tub. Will you never fuck me again if I wear a shower cap? I just blow-dried my hair. Don't look at me."

"You resemble to a poison mushroom."

"Close your eyes. Get in."

He sat in front of her, between her legs. How strange it was to bathe, to boil one's self in a pot. Looking down at his penis just floating there, useless as the egg whites from that soup his grandmother made, the one with all the garlic, he was suddenly so wrecked by sadness, he wished Jane would get out so he could drown himself.

"I was a hairdresser," Jane said. "In another lifetime."

"Do you believe in this?"

"What? No, not like a past life. I mean a former life. Right after high school. I thought I was rebelling. I was not rebelling. I was just doing a job I hated." She gently pushed his butt forward and lowered his head to her breasts. She washed his hair with shampoo that smelled like peppermint, massaging his scalp, his neck, even his ears, and he released a long, shuddering sigh.

*

"You probably find me dark. When I was your age, I found people my age dark. I decided I'd never be dark. I'd never be bitter. I'd never be old. I would never be one of those adults who wouldn't jump in the pool. I'd never go *argh* when I got up off furniture. I'd never say, 'Isn't that something' or 'Aren't you just the sweetest.' I've broken all my rules."

"I don't see you like dark."

"You don't have darkness," Jane said. "That's why you don't see it. That's what drew me to you. Your light."

"My light?"

"No. I don't know. Sometimes I just want life to be poetic. I can't believe I'm one of these people who's so nostalgic for youth she's robbing the cradle. I've always regarded men who do that with disdain."

"I don't see you like old. Why do you think you are old?"

"Do you think you have darkness?"

"Maybe I do not understand what this means." He wanted to talk about something else. The conversation was doing something funny to his pulse. It was beating too quickly in his neck and he was naked. He hoped she couldn't see it. "Let me fuck you," he said. "Turn around. Stand on your knees."

Within the first minutes of knowing her he lied. She was wearing glasses. She was reading a paperback book. She looked like a librarian from an American porno, except she was feverishly gnawing her thumbnail. She had sat with two empty stools on either side of her, instead of at the end of the bar, so he knew that she hoped to be spoken to. He wiped the wood in front of her clean with his rag.

She had a long neck and wore a gold necklace as thin as thread. Her curly hair was caught up behind her and he imagined unclipping it, springing it wild. "Would you like a martini?" he asked. He thought a porno librarian would drink martinis.

She looked startled. She removed her glasses by one stem. Her eyes were blue with some lines on the skin around them. "Where is that accent from?" she asked. "Sorry. Is that a rude question?"

"I come from France."

"How old are you?" she asked. "Sorry. Sorry. Ignore me. Yes. I'd like a martini. How did you know that?"

Guessing people's drinks helped his tips, when he was right. In the beginning, the bartender who trained him had thought it would be funny to teach him to ask customers, "What's your poison?" which he did, having no idea how absurd he sounded, until a manager overheard and said, "What, are you Sherlock fucking Holmes? Cut that out."

"A little bit dirty," the woman was saying. "Not too dirty. I like them less and less dirty the older I get. I want to taste the gin now. I want to make my bad decisions without cover."

When he delivered her martini, she asked him again, "How old are you?"

"Time exists just in the mind."

"If I were creating a caricature of a man, that's what I'd make him say."

"I have thirty."

She tasted the martini and smiled at it. "Perfect."

It wasn't true that he took lots of women home from the bar. The truth was they took him home with them. He spent as few nights as possible in his own apartment, which required at least ninety-eight minutes and three trains to reach, and where he usually slept on the floor. He often looked at the bed, sometimes for so long it undulated in his vision. But he never wanted to enter it.

"There are rules," Jane told him the first time he undressed her. "One rule is that we are equals. This won't be some Mrs. Robinson nonsense."

He had no clue who Mrs. Robinson was.

"I am not your teacher. I am not your mother. I'm no dominatrix. I am not here to give you an experience. If you want an experience, take an Outward Bound trip."

"I agree," he said, because he thought agreeing rather than acquiescing proved that he was her equal. He did not ask what an Outward Bound trip was. He touched her clit the way Iris had liked him to touch her clit. Jane didn't seem to care too much how he touched her clit. She wanted him to tie her wrists together.

"The French do it," she said. "Don't they? With silk? Isn't Lyon famous for silk? Take me to Lyon and bind me in silk."

He tied her wrists together with a long, striped sock.

Even one decade. He would take it. Even one year. One minute.

"You know, I was thirty once."

He shrugged. "And people who have thirty now will one day have forty-two."

"Why are you so literal? I thought the French were philosophical. Where's your inner Sartre?"

The way she said Sartre sounded strange. *Sarch-ra.* "Actually, not everyone has thirty and then forty-two."

He liked saying *actually*. Americans said it every five seconds. They also said *every five seconds* every five seconds.

"Are you telling me I should feel lucky? Because the alternative to turning forty-two is not turning forty-two?"

"You are funny," he said.

"Do you think so?"

"I think you are funny, yes."

"I am funny. I just wasn't sure if you knew that. I studied German in college, but I don't think I would know if someone speaking German was funny."

"Probably someone speaking German is not funny," he said.

When he met Jane, six months and four days had passed since he'd arrived in New York, and in those six months and four days, everyone he spoke with in Lyon had told him to come home. He had never even wanted to go to New York, they reminded him. It hadn't been his dream. And what was he going to do there, open beer bottles and live among the Americans? Why would he want that?

He wasn't sure he wanted that. Wanting felt like something for other people, for children in the presence of cookies. He couldn't want the only thing that seemed worthy of his desire—a chance to tumble backwards; to rearrange the events that had made up his life to date and would make up the rest of it, too; to hurl Iris' death at least six decades into the future. Now the only way he could connect with wanting was by fucking. Sometimes when he thought about staying in New York or not staying in New York, eating or not eating, buying new underwear or wearing the underwear that had thinned to transparency, he remembered the time his brother took him rock climbing in Fontainebleau, how easy it had been to ascend, how afraid he'd felt, how paralyzed, when he made the mistake of looking down. He had wondered what it would cost him, what it would cost the people in his life, if he clung to the rock face forever.

"I bet you take lots of women home from the bar," Jane said.
  "Yes," he said.

Before she sat at his bar with all those empty stools around her, before he got to work that night, he'd smelled Iris while walking to the N train. It happened sometimes, but never for long enough. Always less than a second and the smell was weak like perfume with water. If Iris had worn perfume, he would have bought a bottle instead of relying on passing strangers.

"You all lie," Jane said, crying. "Seventy-five-year-old men. Twenty-two-year-old men. You're all so goddamn disappointing. What else don't I know about you?"
  He wasn't sure what to say. "I love animals," he said.
  "You…? What the hell?" she said, squeezing her eyes shut.
  "I love them too much," he said quietly.
  "Stop saying that. It's 'very much,' not 'too much.' This is good," she said, opening her eyes, getting up, taking the whole sheet with her, leaving him naked and a bit cold. She went to the window and stood looking out, wearing the white sheet like a wedding dress. "This is probably good. I would have gotten sick of correcting you all the time."

It was after he hoisted her onto her own kitchen table, after the first time he came inside her without a condom, that Jane said, "I can tell you had a serious relationship."
  "What do you mean?"

"I can tell by the way you fuck that someone who loved you taught you things."

"Or maybe I didn't need a teacher."

"Why did you break up?" She poured red wine into two glasses. Americans didn't understand wine. The wine in Jane's apartment was always too sweet. The label was a garish yellow and featured some kind of bird that would never exist in the wild. They sat on her couch together and drank her sweet bird wine.

"The majority of relationships do not last for the eternity."

"Men can never explain the nuances of breakups," Jane said. "It's always 'Things just didn't work out,' or 'She was crazy' or 'She didn't respect my work schedule, I have such a busy work schedule!' Was she crazy?"

"She was not crazy."

"Did you break her heart?"

A sudden heat flamed his face from within.

"What?" Jane said. "What just happened?" She spoke quietly. Gently. "Did she break *your* heart?"

He finished the wine in his glass. There was so much sediment, like sand in the bed after a beach day. "I broke hers," he said. "Then she broke mine. But neither of us with the intention to do it."

"One of those on-again-off-again things," Jane said. "We've all been there."

"I want you another time," he said, setting her wine glass on the floor.

Some things he'd noticed about New York women, at least the ones who drank in his bar or walked around Midtown: Many didn't have men and preferred to read a book. New York women said they didn't like condoms, but they must have liked condoms. If you said, "I do not like condoms," they said, "No one likes condoms," while tearing the square-shaped packaging with their teeth. New York women yawned more than French women. New York women were always surprised when he took off his bowtie. They said, "It's a clip-on!" and laughed. New York women looked at you with some suspicion. New York women ate an approximation of ice cream that came from the wall like Jane's bed; it was accessed with levers and then weighed on a scale. Eventually, all New York women wanted to know, "What do you like about me?"

*

"For three months," he said. "Yes."

There was a layer of tears now over Jane's eyes. One tear slipped out.

He touched it on her face. He couldn't believe it. Women cried so easily. Like actors in movies. He wondered if they willed tears by thinking of something else, something very, very sad. Like a war.

"But…why?" she asked.

"I wanted to have sex with you," he said.

Jane always had a lot to do in her apartment. She was often dealing with the murphy bed. She was washing a dish. She was refilling salt and pepper shakers, one black (pepper), one white (salt), both of which said BROOKLYN in red. She was showing him a video on YouTube. She was trying on a sweater. She had many sweaters hanging in her closet, wrapped in clear plastic or in opaque dry-cleaner sacks that zipped all the way around like body bags. It never would have occurred to him to hang a sweater. She would busy herself, talking so much he would forget to pay attention, and he had to pay attention or he'd lose the thread because that was what it was to speak a second language: you had to constantly pay attention or you would find yourself awash in meaningless sounds. Sometimes while talking she would stop in front of him as he sat on the futon (he'd believed only the Japanese had futons) and while telling the most exciting part of her story, her face would become so animated he thought her eyebrows might levitate right into her hairline.

She paused once like this and said, "What?"

"What?"

"Why are you looking at my eyebrows?"

"Because they go up so high!"

She laughed. She sat beside him on her futon and turned to him, tucking her knees beneath her. "What do you like about me?" she asked, smoothing his hair off his forehead.

Without thinking, he said, "You're alive."

"You are not thirty," Jane said to him one early morning after sex. They were lying face to face in the bed she had produced from the wall. The light was blue. Blue light. Blue eyes. That long, naked neck. She looked very beautiful.

"You look very beautiful," he said.

"I realized it after I took those pictures of you last night. You look younger in pictures. Pictures show your true essence. In pictures you look like a child."

"I am not a child."

"Are you twenty-nine?"

He took a deep breath. "I am not twenty-nine."

She swallowed audibly. She pulled the sheet over her hip, and then she drew it up more to cover her shoulder. "You…lied to me?"

"Yes."

"You've been lying to me for three months?"

He hadn't tracked the time he'd spent having sex with Jane. She could have said, *You've been lying to me for five thousand eight hundred ninety-seven years?* and he would have thought, *I suppose I have.*

He would think of Jane one day in the future, when he was nearing the age she would always be in his memory. It would alarm him to realize that Iris, too, would be nearing Jane's age, were it impossible, as it should have been, for a healthy twenty-five-year-old woman to move from Lyon to New York with her twenty-five-year-old husband and die weeks later of a heart attack, in their bed in the middle of the night.

So much that shouldn't have been possible was possible—that Iris could die the way old men died; how quiet the city became when it snowed; that he could hardly even conjure her real face now, only the way her face looked in certain pictures he'd kept: the one in profile from their wedding, confetti raining down; the one she took of herself in the mirror, unsmiling and topless in jeans and bare feet. And now forty had come and gone for him and he'd never had another wife, and had at some point realized he'd outgrown marriage, and wondered if he would have outgrown it even had Iris lived.

How funny, he would think. He didn't feel old at all. Back then he'd felt much older.

The first time they fucked, Jane asked him to speak to her in French.

"What do you want that I say?"

"Doesn't much matter. Tell me what the Eiffel Tower looks like in the mist. Tell me about the Napoleonic code or the feudal laws. Tell me about your back pain. I won't know the difference. You're too young to have back pain, aren't you?" She sighed. "Oh, to be young," she said, biting his neck. "To be young and not know pain."

LYNNE THOMPSON
Warbler

She volunteered to become *ma* to me after calling
the one who birthed but left me, *whore*. I became
an Every Daughter, chipped myself into an
archipelago, skimmed desert sands, daughtered
and disappointed the two of them, being born of
poison oak, distrusting forgiveness but making no
waves. In secret, I redesigned myself as twins—

the first quite quiet, the other wanton and ready
to call out the militia with their weapons never
sharp enough. My *ma* and my *whore* never met
as far as, well you know, and me?—I'm nightmarish
in the undergrowth, like the endangered Whistling
Warbler, one blue note increasing by degree, then
ending, like any other species with one dark wing—

BARBARA TRAN

Buttercups in Foil on the Windowsill

She never set foot in that house, was
on the other side of the world, living
her life as if every day were Sunday, though
given her location this was no
blessing, just another day of
shortages, of thuds in the distance that made
one's mind leap even when one's
body was in bed. One day bled
into another, the ash of intention blowing
into oblivion. To accomplish
anything, one had to leap through the
doorway of existence, existence being
an opening that allowed all you love to leave
as easily as it arrived.

mind

There was a time when, sitting in a parking lot, I could make the parked car in front of me dematerialize. Could drive straight through it, if I wanted to. That was an unwashed time, birdcalls trapped in drawers, matching sets of months when a face could never move a face again. Dematerializing the parked car didn't take faith, it just took thinking about advancing in a particular calm, fierce way. A passing-through that was a dispensing with storytelling apparatus: focus on the object then harbor it no more and move unencumbered through reverie-made space. I could drive through the thing if I really wanted to. A fish might swim under a continent, a bird thread flight through a root system. I never test-drove the knowledge, but not for lack of confidence. Whatever sky there was. Whatever sky there was *was*. Whatever sky there was was flinched with chainsaw synapses. A while ago I taught in a top floor, small room full of left-handed desks. My students and I all leaned funny on our left elbows when we talked about "Thirteen Ways of Looking at a Blackbird." Perhaps I have always been *of three minds*. I guess I never drove through the parked car because somehow I knew, in passing through, it would hurt somebody, but I couldn't figure out who.

reremind

Not my daughter and me saying once, and once again, to remember we need tofu. But more me saying, please call if you're going to be really late. And then we're way past re-, and eyerolls won't undo it, and compulsion won't let the mind rev any way *but*. There's a moth— the greater wax moth—that uses its own echolocation to counter bat sonars. Imagine the trajectories' trajectories. Dictionary founder Samuel Johnson had to do a dance under every doorframe before he could pass through, so he could *gain the crossing*. Thresholds won't stay still, we know this. They follow us, they re-up, thresholds are a pain in the neck. Walking down the sidewalk along a hedge I outline the contour of each sprig by arcing my hand in the air. I draw an echo around the bushes. It feels like a blessing uttered by a curse. Echolalia circumscribes me, it's a little like the re-re kind of reading one does inside Poe's bells-bells. One sane sentence is needed here: Our kitchen right now spreads a beautiful collection of gold, claret, and green cut vegetables. And yes, I'll pick up the tofu at the grocery store.

The Sheep

Shannon Airport was empty at 8:30 in the morning, just twenty of us stumbling off the red-eye from Toronto. A few dark-jacketed employees leaned on brooms to watch the fatigued arrivals. One pointed me to the bus for Limerick, where a small, gray-haired man waited.

"I'm going to Shannon View Farm," I said, "Will you pass by there?"

"Hurry, now, you've got 'aff an 'our to worry abou' thet!" he said and grabbed my backpack, hurrying me up the steps. The bus pulled out of the parking lot, barely faster than I could walk, with a wild clatter. I was gratified to see that the land was emerald after all—emerald and empty. Shannon View, I kept saying to myself, Mrs. Flynn, Bunratty, County Clare—Mrs. Flynn, who had written to me twice in perfect penmanship on lined stationery, and who was the only person whose name I knew in all of Ireland.

Suddenly, the bus stopped and the little gray-haired man called to me–"Hurry, now!" and jumped off to get my pack from the baggage compartment. I was shivering with the fragments of long travel.

"Where am I?" I cried, looking around at empty fields on either side of the road.

"Down there!" he said, pointing at a narrow dirt lane. "Ye'll find it!" He was back on the bus before I could stop him. It was nothing like Mrs. Flynn had described.

As I stood there wondering what to do, a small car drove up and stopped.

"Are ye needin' help, then?" the driver called.

"I'm going to Mrs. Flynn's," I told him. "Shannon View."

"Ah, this is the wrong road!" he said. "Get in. I'll take ye there."

We drove a few miles farther along, and there it was—a farmhouse, a white fence, the sign for Shannon View. When we stopped at the lane, he smiled again and put his hand on my knee, just to see, and I jumped out of the car and grabbed my pack and ran up Mrs. Flynn's driveway.

"Ah, isn't it grand that you're here!" said Mrs. Flynn, and then she put me to bed between cold, white sheets.

I woke up from jet lag to the shock of cold, damp air, and the smell of stew. Arthur and Libby, a retired couple from Florida, were staying in one room, and a pair of silent German women in another. In the evening, we made small talk by the paltry fire. Then I went to my room and bundled up under the covers, my coat around my shoulders. It was wonderful here, I wrote in my journal, overwhelmed by loneliness, "just what I need to really rest."

I was seventeen years old.

The next day, I drove into Limerick with Arthur and Libby. Women who looked a little like my mother did their shopping with scarves tied under their chins, holding down stiff curls. Skinny men in sporting caps and dark suits pored over the football scores in the cramped cafés on the banks of the Shannon. We had tea and biscuits and I bought a copy of Harbison's *Guide to the National Monuments of Ireland*, secretly disdainful of Libby's touristy exclamations. Sharp young men, their hair slicked down and eyes bright with plans, prowled the streets past young women wearing Peter Pan blouses and full skirts and sensible heels. I had only jeans and hiking boots, and my long honey-brown hair hung loose. I looked incandescently foreign, and I was dismayed. I was finally a true outsider after working at it for years.

I had left my parents' home the year before, a teenaged autodidact with a broad vocabulary and a minor police record. Ten years of public school left me raw as a blister, bored, and full of fight. I didn't exactly drop out of high school; I just didn't go back. Instead, with the help of the court-mandated family counselor, I slipped into an experimental program at a nearby state university. It was called Living/Learning, and was based on the Summerhill model of self-directed education. I moved into an old dormitory with about a hundred other dewy freshmen and sophomores. We governed ourselves through long meetings and endless debates about the grand and minuscule concerns of the day. A lot of the students were like me—bright, uncomfortable oddballs who began to thrive in a miniature bubble of our own design. I was a born iconoclast, though I didn't then know the word, and here was a nest of them.

We took classes more or less at will. The small faculty offered various subjects, and students could do independent study, find an internship, or hire an outside expert to teach. We signed contracts for each class, promising to show up and do the work—and mostly, we did. Over the course of a year, a small group of students created a vegetarian cafeteria line for the school, learning the tricks of the restaurant business from scratch. Several long-haired ski bums did an environmental impact analysis of a new ski run on the nearby mountain, and incidentally got to go skiing every day. I bounced from astronomy to semantics, chemistry to sailing. I helped edit a literary magazine and wrote a lot of bad poetry. The college itself wasn't sure how to sort it out; we all got a lot of Humanities credits.

We could take a term abroad. As with everything else, there was no program for this. No curator. If you wanted to travel, you picked a country, designed a project, and then tried to talk a professor into signing your contract. My friend Lorrie set up a language immersion experience with a family in Paris; another friend planned a term on a kibbutz in Israel. My brother, who'd fled the Air Force for L/L, went on a cultural tour of Japan.

I longed for community and justice. I called myself a hippie, a neopagan feminist, a poetry radical. Patty Hearst robbed a bank on my seventeenth birthday, and it seemed fitting; I had kept a catalog of the world's ills for years, and knew all about gasoline shortages, famine in Bangladesh, apartheid, and nuclear testing. My journal began to fill with fantasies of rural refuge; I felt worn out by the world before I could vote.

From the almost infinite distance of a small American college town, Ireland seemed isolated, simple, and clean. I told friends with confidence, if no actual knowledge, that it was a place apart from the world's struggle. I would live on a farm and I would study history—an amalgam of commune and library, scholarly days filled with butter churns. I wrote grand plans for research into the roots of Irish folklore and cultural belief. Then, in what still seems like a miracle, I talked two patient English professors into sponsoring me.

My plan seems close to delusional now, but it went unquestioned by my elders in that pre-litigious time. I had only been on an airplane a few times, had never left the United States, never lived alone—had rarely even been alone for more than a day. This didn't seem like a barrier. I wanted to be a solitary pilgrim. I packed a few changes of rough clothes in a used canvas backpack, and strapped on a sleeping bag with bungee cords. I added a list of postage costs and banking hours, a few hundred dollars of traveler's checks, and Mrs. Flynn's address. That was my preparation—as far as hubris and the optimistic theories of educational reform could take me. I was on my own.

At Mrs. Flynn's farmhouse, I read *The Three Musketeers* under the thin blankets. I felt damp all the time—my sweater, my socks, my hair—and I shivered through the night. During the day, I walked for miles, exploring the confusion of waterways off the River Shannon, its banks lined with old castles and forts. I talked to anyone who would talk to me and in the evenings wrote that the stranger I'd met that day was likely to become a dear friend.

After several days of pretense, not all of it to Mrs. Flynn, I took the bus to Galway: the place for emigrants and sailors. For lonely pilgrims. I had made promises, and so I would work. The bus followed rocky shelves far above a blue-gray sea, shards of white granite breaking through tufts of dark-green grass. Golden streamers of sunlight shifted like smoke from wave to wave. All the streets in Galway led to the sea, like fate: at every turn, I looked straight across the Atlantic.

I had learned by then of the tourist board. A half-dozen travelers crowded the small room, reading pamphlets and checking the bulletin board for ticket exchanges and shared rides. I waited for the busy clerk to notice me and then asked about rooms.

"I'm here to study," I said, hoping that would impress her and get me a good rate.

"God love ya," she said. "Here's the list, and you can check the board." The prices for approved rooming houses were higher than my meager budget could bear. I waited for a space at the bulletin board, watching the milling travelers, mostly young, mostly carrying backpacks, talking in groups of two and three in German and French and languages I didn't recognize. Behind me, I heard an American voice, and turned to see a substantial young woman with thick dark hair and dark eyes.

"Hey," I said, "I'm American too." It was all I could do not to grab her. She introduced herself as Gloria, a schoolteacher from Long Island on a year's sabbatical. She was twenty-five and had a sardonic smile and a bag full of books slung off her arm.

"You dropped out to go traveling," I said with admiration.

"Yes, and I'm running short on funds."

"Do you want to share?" I asked. So we rented a double room together near the university, much better than either of us could afford on our own.

Gloria saved me from study for a time. We went to the Spanish Arch and the Claddagh. She gave me a book of poems by Yeats. I gave her Dumas. We began going to pubs in the evening, something neither of us had wanted to do alone. These were dark, close rooms, with amber lamplight leaving the ornate scrollwork near the ceiling in shadow. Men in sporting caps and dull dark suits filled the bar stools in each place; they were known as the sentries and nursed broad glasses of black Guinness with a tawny foam top through the evening hours. The wall behind each bar was lined with shelves of dark bottles and trays of tall clean glasses, with a big clock above, so no one could complain when the barman called out, "Time, gentlemen, please." We sipped sweet treacly port, "the ladies' drink." In many pubs, we were refused anything else.

We took the bus to Connemara for a night, through miles of crazy-quilt fields with falling rock walls, bog fields, and shaggy mares, and the occasional line of houses like beads in a string. The town of Clifden was a modest place high above the famous bay, and the air blowing through the wet streets was so fresh it seemed to have been newly made. That night, we walked from the farmhouse where we'd found a room down a dark lane to a tiny country pub. Our entrance into a room usually reserved for local men was greeted with a moment of silence and then applause.

"Two ports, please," I asked.

"Ah, but you haven't sung," said one of the sentries, a thin old man leaning back on the bar with his glass of plain in his hand. "Ye 'ave to sing."

I consulted with Gloria, both of us feeling a bit wild with the West. We sang "When the Saints Go Marching In," and then we sang it again, and got our port. And then the entire pub took turns singing to us for an hour, and in between songs I raised my glass and called out, "Slainte ra!" I felt that I had arrived at last.

But the day came when I could put it off no longer, and I walked to the university and presented myself to the research librarian like a gift.

I wanted to study original material, I said, with panache. I was doing research into folklore. She explained that early manuscripts were rare and fragile, and that most were locked away in Dublin. I could read all I wanted from their collection, if I liked, and she pointed me down a long book-filled room—shelf after shelf disappearing into shadow.

I was no kind of student. The public schools in my small hometown had offered no particular challenge. I had read widely, but without guidance, and never had to work hard. Consequently, I had little skill in studying, great gaps in my knowledge, and no way to understand those gaps. I had a lot to prove, and no way to prove it. At home my idea had seemed almost a trifle—Irish folklore and cultural beliefs. I would need to read a few books, of course. With a jolt I realized what my professors had known all along and were willing to let me discover for myself: that I was no more ready to study such a thing than I was to teach it, that research like this was the work of a lifetime, that *original* meant an ancient language. Standing in the silent reference stacks of the University of Galway, I knew for the first time that there were subjects out of my reach, realms out of sight. In one sinking, timeless moment, I realized that to really study this subject required the kind of attention I had never paid to any single thing before.

That day and for many days after, I picked books off the shelves at random. Many were in Irish, and my private embarrassment at not having thought of this was sharp and hot. But I sat down and I started reading where I could about the scattered and vague disasters of the Irish past, both real and felt—stories of the Fir Bolg, the earliest people; the arrival of the Celts and the raids by Vikings; the endless incursions by the English and Scots. I took copious, careful notes. I copied ancient poems and legends and made timelines of important battles and outlined the relationship between versions of a legend. All this in a kind of daze, in a pool of incandescent light in a cubicle beside other silent, solemn readers, hours sliding quietly away in the hushed, high-ceilinged rooms.

Gloria and I decided to go to Dublin, with a stop along the way. She wanted to surprise her never-met second cousin Mrs. Neary, who lived on a farm near Athlone with seven children. And surprise her we did, knocking on the farmhouse door in the middle of the afternoon. Mrs.

Neary was flabbergasted at our arrival, insisting we stay for a few days. "Aren't you bold!" she said, and I preened at the compliment. Bold was exactly how I felt.

We milked cows and played with the children, meeting more distant cousins and drinking quarts of dark hot tea. My father was a lapsed Catholic, and as a little girl I longed to go to Mass with his mother and my four devout aunts decked out in gloves and hats. This was always refused, without explanation. So one Sunday, Gloria taught me how to genuflect, pursing her lips and making me practice over and over in our tiny room in the back of the Nearys' farmhouse, and then we went to Mass with the family. I crossed myself, sang hymns, and bowed my head, searching for roots. Here was my farm; here was my butter churn, my refuge; I couldn't wait to leave.

As we hoisted our packs, bound again for Dublin, Mrs. Neary said, "You should go see the balloons, then."

We made another detour. As the bus swung into the village square in Ballymahon, I looked out the window and saw two perfect orange-and-blue striped teardrops floating on the horizon in the moist glow of twilight. We found a guesthouse, threw our bags in our room, and walked and hitched a few miles farther along to a large estate. The green grass, lit by the falling sun, was littered with silver Bentleys and Mercedes and Range Rovers hitched to small trailers filled with big wicker baskets and coiled ropes. We could hear music from the house, so we simply walked into the drawing room. A small crowd was gathered, drinks in many people's hands. A half-dozen young men sang around a grand piano.

We introduced ourselves to the first people who turned our way, a booming well-fed man named Chris Mullin and his wife, Gay, an impeccably dressed pale woman. They were from Tucson and they took our sudden and rather rumpled appearance as normal; perhaps it was to balloonists. Gay disappeared a moment, and then returned.

"I've got you seats at the table," she said. The fourth Irish Balloon Meet was almost over, she added. They'd run races, competing to see who could get to a pub fastest after ten miles of flight and which basket could hover at a designated altitude for a specific length of time. Of eighteen teams, four balloons had scratched out due to accidents and one had been destroyed, and so it had been altogether a good week of flying. Gay took us around the room to meet the pilots, who named their balloons like children: Denny Crawford, who flew Tulip and had damaged his balloon by crashing into a bog, and Ian Jacobs of the balloon Godolphin, who clutched a trophy, and young Mike Adams, excitable and glad—"I'm with Clarklift! Glad to meet you!" Finally, she introduced us to a handsome silver-haired man named Cyril Murray, a member of the young Dublin Ballooning Club.

At dinner, I only wanted to talk about flying. How could I learn to do this?

"You're not far from the big man, you know," Chris told me. "Don Piccard. He was here earlier but left a few days ago. He has a factory in Roscommon. A balloon factory." Even I had heard the name Piccard, in some vague weather-related way.

"Do call us when you get to Dublin," said Murray's English wife, Rita, writing down the number. "Perhaps we can go up." She meant *up in the sky*, and I could barely breathe.

"Come back in the morning," said Chris, expansive, swinging his glass in a wave. "And call Piccard, if you're interested. He's always looking for help."

We were up early the next morning, walking to the chilly meadow through the last strands of mist. What seemed to be an acre of glowing white and blue nylon was already spread across the grass, surrounded by busy people who nodded and bent back to work. Stand here, someone said; hold this, and I leaned against a thick rope, feet slipping on the wet dawn grass in the shocking roar of propane burners, the loud flap and snap of nylon as the gigantic envelope began to fill and shimmy like a waking beast. Suddenly, the balloon was off the ground and the thick wicker basket stood up and bounced, fell and bounced again as two people clambered aboard. "Now!" I heard someone shout and felt the harsh rope shoot out of my hand as the basket fled into the pale sky.

The rhythm of the Dublin train made the afternoon sun flicker as if reflected by a signal mirror. My head was full of balloons. I'd woken at dawn and looked out upon a bank of black cloud on the horizon, lined with light. As I watched, an upside-down black teardrop rose silently and crossed the face of the copper sun.

We reached Heuston Station and walked into the city heart: stacked rooftops and rows of pale chimneys, bright stucco walls and shiny storefronts, bulbous cars and green double-decker buses, crossing back and forth over the River Liffey on its countless bridges. The river smelled of sewage. I found a pay phone and called Piccard; he wasn't home, but I left a bright message, offering my services. We went to the Irish premiere of *Blazing Saddles* and laughed so hard we almost fell out of our seats, and laughed even harder when we realized that we were the only people in the theater laughing at all.

The next day, we called the Murrays, and if they were surprised to hear from us, they didn't let it show. We took the bus to the suburb of Castleknock where they lived in one of the Guinness mansions. The great white house with its wide white gravel drive was called Oatlands. I was a reflexive if wholly untutored socialist, my ideas about politics the peculiar mix of self-righteousness and hope that is the province of certain bright young people. I didn't want to care about the Bentley and MG parked outside. I didn't want to care about the chandeliers and Persian carpets—or my dirty boots. I laid blame for the world's suffering squarely where it belonged, on the faceless straw men of government and finance. People who lived in houses like this. So, I shook his hand firmly and called Cyril by his first name. He introduced us to Jimmy, his handsome son who worked as a real estate agent, and waved toward a daughter and a nameless younger boy who ran away.

The Guinness family kept a gardener at Oatlands to work the land, a half-acre of figs, vegetables, and flowers. Brendan Crowley was thirty-seven and a native Irish speaker; he was bearded, a bit weathered, often a little drunk. He lived in the mews—seven rooms, five of them empty, with dusty floors and marble fireplaces—and it was to this that the Murrays gently steered our untidy selves. Brendan welcomed us with only a little bewilderment, and we settled in.

Each morning, we rode into Dublin with Cyril or Jimmy. During the day, we toured O'Connell Street and St. Stephen's Green, took tea at Bewley's Café on Grafton Street, went to see the magnificent Geneva Window and the Museum of Modern Art. I found the National Reference Library, with more rooms filled with tall shelves of books I couldn't understand. But I spent a few hours each day reading the work of real scholars who could—about Finn MacCool and his warriors, the tall and fair Tuatha Dé Danaan from the North, the poet Columcille. I read the story of MacDatho's Pig from the Book of Leinster, the *Lebor Laignech*, and began to explore the intricate history of the ancient kingdoms that had become Ireland.

Eventually, I found my way to Trinity College. The Long Room of the Old Library was something to behold: a great tunnel of books, thousands of books shelved in a tall, narrow hall under a curving roof with vertebral spines of dark wood. The spiral stairs led to bays where silent students worked and made me feel vaguely ashamed. The public was not allowed to read there. I could only look at exhibits—the Book of Kells behind glass, a page turned every day.

Each evening, we found our way back to Brendan's involuntary hospitality. Often Jimmy joined us, and we played cards, cooked a few of the vegetables no one else would eat, and walked up the road to the Wren's Nest. Over port and whiskey, I flirted with Jimmy and told Brendan what I had been reading. In turn he told me legends, old wives' tales, and superstitions, and taught me to say *Marbh le tae, agus marbh gan é*—my one true Irish sentiment. *Killed by tea and dead without it.*

"You have to learn Irish or you won't learn anything," he said.

I was studying. But mainly I was reading paperbacks from the penny bins. In between my careful genealogies of mythical queens and diagrams of linguistic relationship, I scribbled movie plots and titles for novels and jokes that made sense only in the moment. I made lists of my ambitions: *1) clown school 2) learn French 3) write for* Rolling Stone *4) fly balloons.*

Somewhere I'd come across a poem called "The Sheep" by Seumas O'Sullivan, who died the year after I was born. It began:

> *Slowly they pass*
> *In the grey of the evening*
> *Over the wet road,*
> *A flock of sheep.*
> *...*
> *Slowly they pass,*
> *And gleaming whitely*
> *Vanish away*
> *In the grey of the evening.*

In the simplest of language, the poet evokes the image of forms appearing and disappearing in the grey, and of *the white days / When we two together / Went in the evening / Where the sheep lay.*

He concludes:

> All white, and go fading
> Away in the greyness
> Of sundering years.

I copied it out carefully and drew a picture with crayons of a flock blocking a country road. I thought it was about sheep.

We left for a time: Carlow to Clonmel, Clonmel to Waterford, Waterford back to Dublin. We were restless circuit riders: Dublin to Mullingar to Ballinasloe across the rounded shoulder of the Republic back to Galway. From Galway up to Roscommon to Ballymurray House, hoping to catch Piccard at home. He was never there. Autumn came in, day by day. The oaks and elderberries blurred into the mist; the empty peat bogs turned golden and then gray. I learned to wash my long hair in cold water in a bathroom sink and pack my canvas sack in a few minutes. I read *The French Lieutenant's Woman.* Gloria gave me Jorge Luis Borges. I gave her *All the President's Men.* Galway to Limerick to Mallow to Killarney and back to Dublin, where we bought Groucho Marx masks and sat on a street corner making a nuisance of ourselves, thinking it a grand joke.

I wrote by the hour, obsessed with the people I'd left at home, with the past and future in equal measure, with all that was wrong and how to make it right, with news of "The Troubles" and the poor and my own lonesome self. The world seemed woven with invisible, radiating lines of force and connection, a matrix in which a single self was both vast and small. "I have the feeling of being a passive floating point in space conveyed to places unknown by everything around me," I wrote. "In relativity there is something about how you yourself are the only absolute; everyone and everything lives and moves relative to you. I pay my £1.70 and sit down and say, 'Here, Roscommon,' and Roscommon conveniently comes, two hours later."

One day, we returned to Castleknock and Cyril Murray greeted us with news: Mike Adams and his partner had been killed in the balloon Clarklift, caught in a freak whirlwind that tore the rip cord open; they fell two thousand feet.

I called Piccard; he wasn't in.

I was avoiding work; Gloria was looking for it, making the rounds of dismal employment agencies that seemed to offer only hopeless secretarial jobs. Then Jimmy's big sister, Tina, who lived in a village to the south, said she knew a wealthy family who wanted a "nanny type" to run errands, chauffeur for the children and so on. An American Catholic schoolteacher? Perfect. In a day it was settled, sight unseen, and Gloria left to work at Borris House just before Halloween.

I was all at once more alone than I had been when I arrived.

I resumed the rhythm, staying for a day or two in one town or another and then moving on. The train compartments had seats for four, facing each other across a table. My fellow passengers read, talked, played cards, or bought tea and biscuits when the girl came through pushing the cart. Many smoked beneath the NO SMOKING signs. When anyone asked, I lied and said I was nineteen. I ate the same cheap food every day: a handful of sultanas, a Toblerone bar, a can of sardines, and a hunk of fresh cheese. I read *Steppenwolf* and *One Flew Over the Cuckoo's Nest* and *Lady Wilde's Ancient Legends of Ireland*. I played a lot of Solitaire, sitting on cold benches outside closed stations, waiting for an early train. Sometimes I crossed the country twice in three days, skipping from Youghal to Killarney to a dim flat in Cork where a crowd of university students made room for me to sleep on the floor and sit at the all-night poker games. Sometimes the challenge of solitude was too much to bear, and I would go back to Oatlands and sit at the table with Brendan, talking until very late, and then fall asleep in my weary sleeping bag on a bare mattress on the floor, in front of a dying fire making faint shadows flicker on the wall.

Now and then I called the Piccards up in Roscommon, and left a polite message. They were never home.

Mostly, I wrote—on buses, in the hushed study bays of libraries, on park benches. I wrote through the whole of chilly evenings in rooming houses. I wrote countless letters, thin blue aerogrammes covered in cramped handwriting, never enough room to say all that needed to be said—euphoric descriptions of the landscape, monologues about social ills and worldly depositions on love. I devoted a great many pages to infatuation and fantasy and the characters of other people. Once, I wrote a letter of apology to my professors; I was sure they were each waiting impatiently for the projects I had no hope of finishing. I made lists of what really mattered and what I would do with my life and where I would go next. I became completely unhinged for pages at a time—with all that might happen, could happen, that I would make happen. *Astronomy*, I wrote. *Go to Andorra. Balloons.*

I walked for miles with a full pack, catching buses in the rain or hitchhiking down isolated country roads for hours to find a bed and breakfast. Then, juddering and tense, I would leave again the next day. I read D. H. Lawrence's *The Trespasser* and Mary Stewart's *The Hollow Hills.* I fell in with another young American woman for a few days. Then I took off to Dingle, heading as far to the west as I could. The colors of the peninsula were a fine tweed of greens and rusts, the water rolling like sky under red and blue and white fishing boats, their masts trim and crowding in the bay. The whole town was jumbled up against the sea, so remote that it had once minted its own coins; Dingle had been a great smuggling town. I went to the movies with a young man from the Tourist Office and left the next day, heading for Borris House and Gloria and not being alone.

Borris House was in the valley of the River Barrow, near a village called Muine Bheag—once called Bagenalstown for its founder, William Bagenal, who had been seized by a vision of Versailles and set out to make a town of the same name and architectural worth. He did not achieve this. Gloria picked me up at the tiny Muine Bheag train station in her employer's big car, gave me a quick hug and pulled back. "Man, this town is filled with gossips," she said, by way of hello. "No privacy. Everything I do gets up to the house."

On a nearby hill, I could see the big stone castle higher than everything in the valley, a giant gray box trimmed with parapets and chimneys against the stormy sky. Jimmy's sister Tina, it turned out, was married to Andrew MacMorrough Kavanagh Leinster, descendant of the ancestral kings of Leinster, one of Ireland's four ancient kingdoms. Andrew and Tina and their baby daughter, Aiofe, lived in the converted mews in back of the house. Over generations, death duties and taxes almost took the house out of the family hands. An unfinished painting by Rubens had once hung in the bathroom to be used as a target for wet sponges by the children; it was sold to save the house. Now the king's descendant worked the land and rented the mansion out. Gloria worked for their tenant.

We drove slowly up the winding gravel drive, and the head housekeeper stepped out to meet us, her crisp white apron covering a gray dress. She took my hand and said, "You are *welcome* to Borris," in a murmuring, respectful voice. The cold entry hall echoed with the noise of children racing through, and I could see into the sunny kitchen where several young women in uniform worked.

Gloria's employer was the American film producer Michael Todd, Jr., a big bluff man with a degree in philosophy from Amherst and his daddy's Oscar. Todd shook my hand and disappeared, and his wife, Susan, a short curly-haired woman who preferred to stay in the kitchen and supervise the preparation of grand meals, said a shy hello. I followed Gloria up a wide winding staircase; she was laughing as she watched me take it in through the huge windows as we climbed: the collection of Ming vases and Renaissance art, the massive stables, the separate chapel, the 680 acres of moist green lawn and woods. She showed me the library, with its shelves so high that a rolling ladder was required and pointed out the illuminated manuscripts inside a glass case.

Gloria had her own suite of rooms on the second floor. A room had been made up for me on the third floor in what used to be the servant's quarters, up the back scullery stairs, with a fireplace and heavy, dusty curtains and a big creaky bed. We went out for a tour of the grounds, and ran into Andrew, a lanky man in his mid-twenties with a high forehead, long nose, red cheeks and big squirrel teeth: to me, the unmistakable marks of aristocracy. He wore a filthy torn sweater and wellingtons. A pair of huge russet-colored Irish setters bounded beside him. We said hello, and he marched on toward the stables.

"He's a *laird*," Gloria whispered to me as we walked away, with a tiny smile behind her hand. From then on, I always called Andrew "the Earl," an ironic confusion of history that I did not understand for years.

Gloria ran the family errands and Sue ran the kitchen. Michael spent hours talking to New York or Los Angeles and loudly cursing the P and T, the government utility that combined post and telephone into one labor of Sisyphus. When Gloria wasn't busy, we rode around the front fields with proper English saddles and black helmets or carried little wicker baskets into town to shop at stores bordered by hedges and windrows. On nice days, we went for long hikes over the soft irregular fields where the pheasants fed in the morning, down into the vale and woods past old mill wheels. But she was often busy, and then I wandered the great house alone, exploring the closed wings falling into disrepair. Sometimes I ended up in the library, a warm room with overstuffed chairs where I could play classical records on the turntable. Once, when I was sure no one was watching, I snuck into Michael's study and picked up the heavy gold Oscar he kept on the mantel there.

I was driven into self-reflection like a cow down a chute—driven by isolation and discomfort, by having no clue. I began to experience something new. Very distantly, and long before I could have explained it, I saw what it was like to be disappointed in one's self and keep on going. I recognized obstacles even as I placed them, found answers even as I asked a question, then promptly found a way to forget. I understood and then forgot that I'd understood; this seesaw between knowing and forgetting would become one of the rhythms of my life. Briefly I saw that it might be easier to live without the ceaseless examination that I couldn't seem to stop. I saw that I could forget—or I could remember. My choice. "There is so much in me, abstract and instinctive and unformed," I wrote. "I want to take my life into my hands. I want to do everything. I want to make realities out of my dreams." I wanted most of all to hold on "to my fleeting feeling of being a floating point moving effortlessly in and out of turmoil, where things will happen of their own accord."

Every time I returned to Borris House, the third-floor room was waiting. They simply let me in. We ate Thanksgiving dinner in the long, cold dining hall framed by tall windows with the Leinster crest in stained glass, lit by chandeliers and candlelight. Michael and Andrew talked about the European economy. I drank a glass of wine, and another, and announced to the table that money wasn't real. I knew there was wrongness in the world—how could it matter if London was supporting the dollar or not? Everyone turned to look at me. Money is just pretend, I said. What we should do is feed hungry children, I said. *Eat the rich* is what I meant. Does the currency of Spain really mean anything? I asked the table, expansively. Does it really mean anything at all?

I think of this now and I am stunned by the kindness and the patience and by how much I missed. I'd bent over the slowly turning pages of the Book of Kells, but I barely glanced at the shelves of Borris House, where the illuminated history of the Kingdom of Leinster sat in one case and another held a great drinking vessel made of ivory, the twelfth-century Kavanagh Charter Horn. I sat beside the king's descendant at meals and never asked him a thing worth asking. Whitely they gleam for a moment, and vanish away.

I left the next day for Dublin, where Oatlands always let me in.

One day, Cyril offered me a job. He knew I was running out of money, that I wanted to stay in Ireland, that I was still trying to catch up to the Piccards.

"You'd have to clean up a bit," he said.

I had paid just enough attention to know that he worked in the city, that he wore a tailored suit and tie every day. I was not sure what he did for a living. Doing what? I asked. A job! A job would mean I could stay.

Kruggerands, he explained. He dealt in currency, mostly from South Africa. I could do phone orders and reception at the office. I was almost broke, and I couldn't say no. But I had boycotted everything from grapes to Nestle candy bars, and I knew about apartheid. *Kruggerand* was an epithet, and I couldn't say yes. I told Cyril I needed to finish my projects first.

I returned to Galway where the tourist season was long over, and at last found a good room in the little beach suburb of Salthill, in a big warm house with a stereo and shower and piano. I could walk to the university along wide streets lined with white stucco walls, the pavement always glistening with the night's rain and the restless bay below lapping along the shingle.

Perhaps it was the shrinking days, foggy and gray and growing dark without ever having grown light. Perhaps I'd worn out the agitation, or just gotten warm for the first time in months. But finally I settled down to study in a way I'd never studied before. I didn't just read—I learned. I read parts of the Book of Invasions, an ancient imaginary history in which Ireland is the bastard child of fantastic races. I found a translation of *The Book of the Dun Cow*, Ireland's oldest existing manuscript, a hodgepodge of fragmented legend and religion and dream. I read parts of the later Fionn Ballads and part of the Red Branch Cycle. I read about Guaire the Hospitable and Charles the Bald and Cuchulain, the great fighter who tied himself to a pillar so he could die standing up. I read from old books, from precious books, wearing white gloves, under supervision; I learned in a mix, upside-down, without order, without plan, but I learned.

A few weeks later, we were back in Dublin together for a long weekend, Gloria briefly freed. We walked down to the Christmas Fair and thought about the future. I had told Cyril I needed to think about it, knowing somehow that the offer had been a strange one for him, an offer he made in spite of the obvious drawbacks. I couldn't say yes and I couldn't say no.

That night, he took us to the balloon club meeting, and there was Don Piccard, a lean man with sharp eyes. Without any preamble, I told him that I would work for free if he would teach me the trade.

Sounds good, he said, turning toward the half-dozen others waiting for his attention. *How about April?*

I returned to Borris House for an early Christmas in a strange mix of exhilaration and panic. I had only a few dollars left. I would need to go home—my return ticket was still in the bottom of my filthy pack—and say my goodbyes and find my way back by spring. I would learn to fly. We watched *Les Miserables* on television, and then ate a long feast of three-inch steaks and cranberry ices, with everyone together around the table. I gave Gloria a book of paintings from the Munich Gallery and she gave me two books by Borges and a wooden spoon.

The next day, we walked for an entire afternoon. Roses were still blooming here and there in the valley. We talked about fate and cosmic intervention and karma. I talked, mostly—about love and justice and my long lists, Cyril and Kruggerands and balloons. The earliest possible moment, I told her. I would be back at the earliest possible moment.

One should fling oneself with complete trust into the arms of the universe, I said.

"We have to throw ourselves into everything," I said, standing on a broken railroad trestle. "That's when the universe will take care of us."

"We'll fling ourselves," said Gloria.

"Close our eyes. Trust. Fling!"

"It's a deal," she said. We walked on.

"We must grasp what we can," I wrote that night, "what by hazard can be ours."

A writer is, in large measure, a witness, and one becomes a writer in part by seeing, and seeing the fact that one sees. You record and know yourself to be recording, and, thus, are doubled: a witness to the world and a witness to one's own self equally, witness and recorder at once. In time you learn to slide back and forth from the world's perception of the self to the self's perception of the self without preferring one to the other. A writer is that peculiar kind of introvert who needs to be alone and has a lot to say at the same time. The questions I carried like open wounds, the conundrums of science and politics and the meaning of our oldest stories, are existential questions at heart—spiritual questions, in fact, that we are bound by nature to ask. Without knowing the words, I knew it wasn't exactly happiness that I sought. I was often lonely and confused and I wore the skin of *other* like a coat, but I felt a kind of spaciousness I'd never known before. In Ireland I began to sense that loneliness might be, in some way, necessary to me. I began to see that the world I longed for would demand something from me in return. That sacrifices would be made. In fragile, glancing moments, I saw my own self as incomplete, saw that I was a partial creature, and that this was both natural and good. The themes of my life were being written in my journals of Ireland, though I had no way to know that then. I was discovering the buried treasure of what would matter in my life.

As long as we live, we come upon unmarked forks in the road. One never knows until much later—if at all—which way is best. There is so much ahead to be missed, so few things to be caught, much to gain and much to lose. It is quite impossible to know ahead of time, and if we did, however could we choose? To go here is to not go there, to do this is to not do that. We suffer not so much from the *what* of our losses as from the mere fact of loss itself. A faint sorrow colors the snapshots of memory like a fading sun colors the sea.

Just before I left, I called Don Piccard again, to make arrangements for my return. His wife told me they had decided it would be at least a year before they could take on another person. I thought of calling Cyril and asking if the job still stood, if there was any way I could stay, if I could stay after all. But I did not.

I was crushed. I was glad. That was the last bit of rope in my hands.

To the Girl Rocking Out So Hard in Her Minivan that She Almost Rear-Ends My Minivan

Ignore that I am invisible to you,
a man old enough to call a girl a girl when I see one.

Ignore how I am held up by a half-Windsor
slouched under teeth yellow as a work day is endless.

Ignore the depth of my voice and listen. It's not the van.
Or the bumper. Or the rubber left on a street

we both will drive days and weeks and years from now.
This will not be a lecture, but an epithalamion

for a vow you know nothing about, but that circles the bare
tendril of your finger, whispering a life that's the best of yet-to-come.

Don't believe it. Look at me, at what, unlike you, I have chosen
to drive that I may carry others. Listen to the wail of my clothing

hanging on this frame, to the hair short as a paycheck, to a face
shaved every day to scrape the man clean to sketch anew

the delicate line between me and the unknown—
and enjoy your hair. I watched it,

saw it furl and boil in the rearview, sure as I knew I'd run
a red light to keep from soaking the thrust

of your clueless rocking. And when you pounded your brakes,
mouth oblate, soundless and still, the radio oblivious

to the tingling rush in your chest, I knew the ache there—

you, a girl who needs nothing just as a sky needs no sun—

and when the cold found its home, burrowed
as if for the first time, when you knew what harm you carried,

your eyes flashed with a light that will burn you to ash,
smudge your eyes and wilt your hair, tug at your cheeks

and sorrow your hands, wear at you like the loving grave
you know you step into, if only to seal it so others may walk

over you. Only drummers and parents own vans,
and while you rocked, your hands never left the wheel.

No drummer alive can drive without rhythm when moved
like you were. So the van is a gift, from some father or mother,

some parent who you know thinks about you in the car,
but you have no clue how they *think* about you in that car,

radio loud, light turning to amber, rain sheen across the lanes,
dark horror of the deer sprinting, the drunk listing over center—

If we could just pull to the side of the road, if you would not see
the tie and baggy eyes and paunch and drive hellbent to *cree-pee*,

if you would roll down the window a crack and lower the volume
we both feel in our chests, I would share what I know of abandon,

for how I know hair can thrash, how the heart lunges,
slouches into beat and strum and crash, and I will sing

of blood of two running in one heart, how that pulpy muscle
will pulse and sprint for what can be lost, for what can fail,

for how a life not your own but entirely yours can slow you down,
how joys are never pure, how the head that bangs one day looks up.

JIM WHITESIDE
Shovel

Same one we'd kept
in the garage

or in the toolshed
my whole life, same

loose handle, same tarnished
blade. I'd seen my father

sharpen it on the bench grinder,
sparks flying, to cut

through roots or hardened
soil. Same one I'd used

to replant our overgrown
geraniums one spring,

from the front of the house
to the back lot. Now,

I'm riding shotgun,
my sister in the back seat,

the box with
his ashes in her lap.

To the small family
cemetery, to bury

our dead. My father.
How big to make the hole,

how deep? That same jumping
motion as when

I was a kid, same
feet to the blade,

my whole weight pushing
further into ground. Taking turns

to move the dirt, opening
the box, and cutting open

the bag they'd put him in.
I think of the later

months, his sick body
and failing organs,

distended belly. How he grew
so weak, and so foreign—

all that remains
are the bones,

ground to pebbles.
My sister asks,

*Is it weird if I want
to touch them?*

We all do.

Running our hands
through the rough sand,

our closest thing
to him. I take the tool

by its rough handle,
pile over the dirt,

make even.

MARK WINEGARDNER
Pucker Factor

Just before noon on a Friday that is, better late than never, the first perfect day of spring, a bell on the Commons starts to ring. For years this bell had been bolted inside an Erie & Lackawanna train engine, riding the rails along the Cuyahoga River, less than a mile to the west of here, saving daydreamers and fools from themselves. It was salvaged and installed on the Commons, a bowl-like valley surrounded by boxy institutional buildings, all sporting curve-free midcentury architecture that is as blandly suitable for a hospital, a courthouse annex, or a jail as it is for a state university. The bell is housed in a complementary brick structure, flanked by half-filled planters and hapless landscaping. It's waist-high. Anyone can ring it, though rarely does anyone do so just for the hell of it. People call it the Victory Bell. This is not ironic. This is Ohio, 1970. It's literal. The bell gets rung after football victories, which are infrequent, and, as now, to let students know there's something happening here.

Alice Graves rushes from class with a cheap, battered briefcase stuffed with ungraded freshmen themes. She's a tall, blond, braless grad student with rose-tinted sunglasses, and a vertical scar the length of the left side of her face that somehow only makes her more attractive. She's working on a PhD dissertation about covert radical politics in the novels of Jane Austen that even her students can tell she'll never finish.

Alice doesn't know who came up with the idea to bury the Constitution. Probably someone from the crowd at the Haunted House—a gothic monstrosity on Columbus Street that's become the town's semiformal intellectual and cultural hub, a hangout for SDS leaders now that the group has been banned from campus, and a crash pad for like-minded out-of-towners. Alice has been spending more time there herself (whether as a means of not writing her dissertation or out of sincere affiliation, she'd rather not think about), but she'd found out about this particular rally this morning, from a leaflet on her windshield. Now, as forty or fifty people gather around the bell, Alice finds a good spot on Blanket Hill and sits down to watch and eat her lunch.

On the periphery of the Commons, sorority girls chase frat boys wearing derby hats, trying to tackle and kiss them. This is a May 1 custom at Kent State. The Greeks, prosaically enough, call it Derby Day. It's also May Day, of course, which is of interest to the town's Commies, of whom there are exponentially fewer than would be imagined by the townspeople celebrating Law Day, a small-town Ohio May 1 tradition in which many businesses close shop to honor both the concept of law and order and the brave souls who risk their lives to make that cherished notion possible. America is a more peculiar land than even its most fervent celebrants and critics will ever know.

"Miss Graves?"

Alice squints up at a huge man with a jet-black Jew-fro, a full beard minus the chin hair, a backpack slung over his shoulder, and carrying a guitar case. He'd been a student in one of her classes that fall. It takes her a moment to remember his name. "Don Sokolove, right? You wrote that expository paper about Captain Beefheart."

"Right. On *Trout Mask Replica*," he says. "I can't believe you remember."

Neither can she. It must have been the topic. She'd asked the students to explicate the merits and/or appeal of a pop-culture text. Most picked popular Hollywood movies or the Beatles.

"I remember the good ones," Alice says, though she has no memory of the paper itself.

"Thanks," he says. He's older than most freshmen—thirty, she'd guess: a little older than she is. She's had several older students in her classes—for the most part, a consequence of layoffs at nearby steel mills, auto plants, and tire factories.

"Actually," he says. "I go by Donny. Not Don."

"As you may remember," she says. "I go by Alice, not—"

"Miss Graves," he says. "Yeah, sorry. I could never bring myself to call you Alice."

Under the beard, Donny seems to be blushing. He'd been quiet in class but, if memory serves, he'd done well: A-, B+, something like that. She's an easy grader. It's a huge time-saver.

"Are you here for the rally?" she says, nodding toward it. "Could be educational. Entertaining, anyway."

He looks over at the people milling around the bell. Donny's posture gives him the air of someone who doesn't fit in anywhere and is never unaware of it. "Sure, why not?" he says. "Alice." He's got one of those big, guileless, Midwestern smiles even the calamities of life can rarely annihilate. "I just got out of class. I have band practice, but…I mean, not for an hour or so."

He sits down beside Alice on the grass. She hadn't meant for him to join her. She was only trying to teach, to enlighten.

As soon as she mints this thought, she knows it's not true. She'd wanted him to sit next to her. Maybe it's the guitar case. Maybe it's the work boots and broad shoulders and that sorry mop of hair. Maybe it's his gnarled right hand. There's something haunted and soulful about the guy. She's always been drawn to damaged people. She feels herself blush as well. Her scar glows. She offers him half of her egg-salad sandwich. He takes it.

The first speaker is a balding white teaching assistant from the history department who starts out with announcements about an upcoming underground film festival, next week's ecology symposium, and a rally later that afternoon by the Black United Students to rap about "the coming revolution in AmeriKKKa." He clears his throat and dutifully points out that the BUS spells America with three K's. Alice looks for black people in the crowd. There aren't any.

"Probably that one'll be better," Donny says. "The brothers are better organized."

She looks at him. This is not the sort of thing she'd have ever expected him to say. "What?"

"They've seen more, y'know?" Donny says. "Been thinking about it longer."

Alice has never been to a BUS event.

"I don't want to be a jerk," Donny says. "But…y'know. The tanks and riots tore apart their neighborhoods, not…uh. These people's."

Just then, a fraternity boy stumbles and goes rolling past them down the hill. He makes no attempt to rise. A moment later a squealing brunette dives on top of him and gives him a kiss.

"Or those people," Alice says. The brunette, Alice realizes, just cut her eleven o'clock class. "At any rate, I can't go. To that rally. I have a three o'clock class."

"Band practice," Donny says, rapping the knuckles of his good hand against the guitar case.

Beside the Victory Bell, the T.A. waves a copy of the Constitution like a hanging judge brandishing a wanted poster. The Constitution itself looks as if it's been torn from a middle-school history book. He starts shouting, trying to spur everyone into being as angry as he is about President Nixon and the just-announced invasion of Cambodia. He says he's a founding member of a group called WHORE. When he explains what that stands for, he lets go of the button on the bullhorn; all Alice catches is the R and the E—"racism" and "exploitation." The man calls the Chicago Eight and the Black Panthers "true friends of liberty," and the crowd cheers.

Alice looks around again. She does see three black kids in the crowd now. Several others are walking by but keep walking. It's a buckskin-and-bead freak crowd. Hippies. Artsy white kids. Three-fourths male. On the edge of the Commons, pretty girls in miniskirts and fishbelly-white legs are still racing around after boys clutching derbies to their heads.

The second speaker is a young chemistry prof with an impossible-to-place Slavic or possibly fake accent. He waves his arms like a person with a nervous condition. He's dressed in fatigues and a green army cap. He has a fat cigar in his mouth. "This," he shouts, "is my Castro costume!"

That provokes a roar of approval and laughter.

"Costume," Donny mutters, shaking his head.

"It's theater," Alice says, though, in fact, the chemistry prof is already on her nerves as well.

"Maybe that's the problem," Donny says.

"Don't be uptight, OK?" she says. "Or negative."

"I'm not uptight or negative, either one," Donny says. "I'm just… paying attention."

"That's *exactly* what an uptight person would say."

"At least I'm not negative."

"I don't know." She looks at him over the top of her sunglasses. "You're not *not* negative."

"Right on," he concedes. "But that sentence sure is," he says, which is when she's pretty sure she'd given him an A.

The chemistry prof rattles off Communist slogans spiked with bitter wisecracks about the government. The crowd is pushing a couple hundred now and eating it up.

"I will say," Donny says, "this guy is a natural public speaker."

"True," Alice says, "although I could do without the spastic arm-waving. And the costume."

Donny smiles.

"So what kind of band are you in?" she says.

"Hard to say," Donny says. "Beyond calling it rock and roll, we're still figuring that out. Actually, one person in the group—not me—wouldn't even call it that. Anyway, so far, all we've done is practice."

"This band have a name?"

"We're down to a couple options," he says. "Our first gig is tomorrow, though. So I guess we'll have to settle on something." He touches his arm as if what he's about to say has just occurred to him. "Hey, you ought to come. It's in the Tri-Towers. I can get you on the guest list."

I bet you can, she thinks. "Wait, isn't that a dorm? Tri-Towers?"

"To be honest with you, I'm not sure. I live off campus."

"I'm not sure it's a good idea," she says, "for a grad student to go to some party in a dorm."

"It'll be fine," he says. "Really: you should come."

Alice tells him she has a ton of grading to do this weekend. This he seems to accept. He tells her he didn't mean to come on too strong. She lets that go—lets it just hang out there.

Now the history T.A. again comes forward. He introduces another grad student from his department—a stocky guy with a crew cut who could have fit in with the derby-hatted frat boys. The first history T.A. calls the man with the crew cut a hero and then pauses to tell the crowd to stop booing. The first T.A. then says that, as a member of the 101st Airborne, the stocky man had won the Bronze Star and an Infantryman's Badge. The crowd boos even harder.

"Listen to me!" the T.A. shouts. "This man? This man is *cool*. Dig? He's cool. This man is one of *us*."

Donny lets out a deep breath.

"What?" Alice says, frowning.

"Nothing."

"For your information," Alice says, "not everyone who went over there is a pig."

Donny purses his lips and nods. "Yeah," he says. "Maybe."

The stocky man takes the bullhorn. He has a soft voice. From where Donny and Alice sit, it's tough to hear him. But then the man chokes up in the middle of a sentence and looks down. When he starts speaking again, his voice is much louder. "I'm so *disgusted* with the behavior of my country in invading Cambodia," he says, "that…" He pauses and reaches into his shirt pocket. "These are my discharge papers, OK?" he says, unfolding them. "I *earned* the right to burn these papers—"

The crowd bursts into applause.

"—and, *goddamnit*, I'm going to do it!"

All around the Victory Bell, people are reaching into their pockets and throwing matchbooks at the stocky man, even though he's already pulled out a lighter.

The stocky man lights the papers on fire.

Others in the crowd rush forward to light things too—draft cards and blue books and what looks to Alice like blank notebook paper. The increased fervor seems to have cleared away the Derby-Day kids.

"I wish I could burn all the papers I have to grade," Alice says, holding up her briefcase. "But I'd probably get sacked."

"You could always burn your bra," Donny suggests.

She frowns. Is that some crack about women's lib? About how small her boobs are? Or a joke about her already being braless?

"Sorry," he says.

She looks him in the eye and plucks at the front of her blouse. It's an act of defiance, meant to throw him off his game, to ensure that he's the one on the defensive.

He's blushing again. "Kidding," Donny says.

"Ha ha," she says, trying to keep her face as blank as she can.

As people begin to run out of items they feel like burning, a professor wearing a braid and John Lennon glasses and dressed sort of like a pirate grabs the megaphone and bravely urges students to bring on a revolution by refusing to go to class or take exams or accept grades or listen to "bullshit lectures by bullshit profs."

"You should know," Alice mutters.

"You know that guy?" Donny says.

"No," Alice says. "Not really." She screws up her mouth. "Sort of."

"Ah, OK," Donny says. "Sort of."

A redhead with an Indian headband and hair down to the seat of her overalls spray-paints STRIKE on the bricks beside the bell.

"It's not like that," she says. And, in truth, it had only been like that for a little while and is long since over.

"I didn't say it was like anything."

Beside the bell, the grad students pretend to start digging. This is more theater. The hole has already been dug.

"Probably someone's daddy's yard man, huh?" Donny says.

"Someone's what?" For a moment, she takes this as a crack. Her family had—*has*—black maids and yard men. But she doubts she ever said anything in class about coming from money. He couldn't know that.

Donny points. "All I mean is, somebody already dug that hole."

"So?" she says.

"So nothing," he says. "It's just odd. I'm not being critical."

The first history student retakes the bullhorn. He points the shovel—shiny; clearly purchased for the occasion—right where Alice and Donny are sitting. "Now, I want you all to welcome the pig who comes to all our rallies!"

Oddly, Donny flinches. Alice turns around to flip off the potbellied campus cop behind them, over by Johnson Hall, leaning against the side of his Jeep and taking notes.

"Say hello to J. Edgar Pig!" the T.A. says. In sloppy near-unison, the crowd obeys. Alice isn't the only one flipping the cop off, but she is in the minority. Most people make the peace sign instead, which, with his left hand, Donny does too.

The Constitution is safely underground now. The chemistry prof takes back the bullhorn and raises his fist. "*Stop this war!*" he chants. This is the finale. "*Stop this war!*"

It catches on, barely and only for a few moments.

As it fades, the crowd is buzzing that there's going to be action downtown tonight. Where that rumor started, who knows?

By then, the crowd's breaking up.

Donny stands and offers Alice his hand. She accepts. He pulls her to her feet. He's as strong as he looks and taller than she is.

"So," Donny says. "Any chance I can talk you into—"

"Going downtown tonight?" she says. It's a preemptive move. She doesn't want to commit to going to his band's crummy gig in some dorm. Which would be a date. A weird one. "Just to dig the scene and have a drink?"

He runs his good hand through his hair, somehow, and smiles. They name the time and she takes it as a good sign that he suggests Orville's. He bows, mock-chivalric, and they go their separate ways.

After class, Alice tries to work on her dissertation but falls asleep at her kitchen table and wakes up with her face planted on the typewriter and impressions of the keys on her cheeks and forehead. It's dark. Just like that, as usual, Alice is running late—about an hour, best case. She calls the bar but it's too loud at Orville's for them to hear her. There's no way to get in touch with Donny. Even if he's gone home, she doesn't have his number. She's in the shower before it occurs to her that the easiest way out of this is to stand him up and lie about it if she ever sees him. What are the odds that he'll even still be there? Even if he is, why would she want to have anything to do with some-one who'd wait and hour, hour and a half, to have a drink—not even a date, necessarily—with a woman he hardly even knows beyond her cranky, harried classroom persona?

She shaves her legs and puts on good underwear (including a simple white bra), a flowered cotton shirt and bell-bottoms and takes a con-dom in her purse. You never know. She tells herself it's OK. She tells herself she needs to get out more.

Even before she gets to the train tracks that go through the center of town and separate campus from the Strip, Alice can hear that it's a wild night down there, though she chalks it up to the celebration of the end of another horror-show snowbelt winter on this, the year's first perfect day of spring. When she gets there, it looks as if she's right: a typical Friday night only more so. A police cruiser is parked at either end of the Strip—half the town's fleet but only one more than usual. In between, the street is overflowing with young people. A biker gang with leather jackets identifying them as THE CHOSEN FEW is popping wheelies and rodding around—more like the night's complimentary entertainment than any kind of threat. There's a smattering of true believers walking around with raised fists and waving signs about Nixon and piggery, but for every person here to foment revolution, there's twenty propelled by hormones and the prospect of cold beer. All the bars look packed. The Kove's crammed with obstreperous Greeks. People in Big Daddy's and the Ron-De-Vou are screaming at some basketball game on the televisions. Upstanding squares and preps—the crowd she'd hung out with as an undergrad back at Florida State—are lined up trying to get in to Pirate's Alley. A power trio that sounds a lot like the James Gang (Kent alums who used to play here all the time and put out an album last year) metes out a wall of guitar gallantry upon the freaks at JB's. This is one of two bars Alice goes to, but—given the context, the rally—if Donny had picked it, Alice would have been let down by the obviousness of the suggestion. Orville's had once been a townie bar—the go-to saloon for lumberjacks who'd lived in a dorm out the back door and behind an alley. The dorm had recently been converted to studios for art majors, but Orville's shot-and-a-beer, pickled-egg ambience has stubbornly endured.

When Alice gets there and worms her way in, Jimi Hendrix's "Crosstown Traffic" is blaring from the jukebox and Donny Sokolove is still at the bar, reading a paperback copy of *The Feminine Mystique*. "You're still here," she shouts in his ear. "I'm so sorry."

"Sorry I'm here?" he shouts back. "Or sorry—"

"I'm late. Obviously," she says. She makes a face meant to convey the absurd and hectic nature of life in general. "I lost track of time." She pantomimes typing. "Writing."

Donny nods and asks her what she's drinking. She asks what he's having. He holds up his near-empty glass and says Old Grand-Dad, rocks. Whenever Alice orders a white wine, which is what she likes and almost always orders, she thinks how much she doesn't want to be a girly nothing who drinks white wine, whereupon she's filled with self-loathing. She gestures to the bartender to refill Donny's drink and bring one of the same for her. Donny doesn't seem surprised or impressed. She can't believe she's deigned to notice this or care about it, whereupon she's filled with self-loathing.

Donny points to the TV over the bar. "Great game," he says. "NBA Finals. New York/LA They're going to overtime." He holds a hand just over the top of her head. "You look like you might have played basketball."

She frowns. She hates this. Just because she's tall. She did play basketball, but, still. She hates this. "Not really," she says. "A little." She imposes a similar hand gesture on him, only with both hands and just outside those shoulders. "You look like you might have played football."

"A little," he says. "My dad was a coach and I sort of rebelled against it." He shrugs. "It was a mean thing to do."

"How so?" she says. "Sounds like you were trying to find the scene that was for you."

He shakes his head. "I know it's not hip," he says, "but I loved football. It was fun. I was just stupid."

They've adjusted, the way people do in a loud bar, and are no longer yelling into each other's ear but face-to-face, in a remarkable imitation of a normal-volume conversation.

"So," she says, picking up his book from the bar, "is this for my benefit?"

He gives her an uncomprehending look and then recovers. "It's for a class," he says.

She picks it up, though of course she's read it, and trying to see what he's highlighted, though of course he might have bought it used. She hands it back to him. "I'm impressed."

"Don't be," he says. "I like the class and all, but, I gotta be honest, I took it to meet women."

She laughs. She knows she's supposed to be offended, but, Jesus H. Fuckchrist, it's so much work to marshal your feelings so they conform to what your head tells you is appropriate.

It's murder being the daughter of a shrink.

"And?" Alice says. "How's that going?"

Their drinks arrive. Donny raises the glass with his messed-up right hand and takes a healthy pull. Alice has a sip from hers. He must be right-handed, she thinks. Why else expose it like that except instinct? The hand must be why he left the factory, using disability money to go back to school.

"I'm one of three men in the room," Donny says. "It's like at that rally this afternoon, when they mentioned black people and the white people craned their necks, looking to see if there were any around. If they see one—"

"They immediately look away," she says.

He laughs. "Don't feel bad," he says. "I did it too."

"Piece of My Heart" comes on the jukebox, silky-smooth, different enough to make Alice cock her head.

"Erma Franklin," Donny says. "Aretha's sister." He shrugs. "It's the original." Donny takes a gulp of bourbon. "Anyway, the class. There's this one guy who's made no secret that he's only there to get laid," he says. "So he's a goner. Guy number two has his eyes on guy number one. Me, I don't say much in class, and—"

"I remember," she says.

"And so, at a certain point, it dawns on them that, unlike First-Row Romeo, who's too interested, and Second-Row Steve, who's not interested at all, and all the guys in the world who aren't taking this class," he says, tapping the book. "Well, you know. There I am."

She rolls her eyes and takes a proper slug of her own drink. She'd expected to choke on it, but the melting ice has made it easy to swallow. Delicious, even.

"I don't want you to get the wrong idea" Donny picks the book off the bar and waves it. "I really like the class. And I haven't—"

She puts a hand up for him to stop. "Don't," she says. She jiggles her glass. What she'd meant this to convey was that this was just a drink they were having together, that he didn't owe her any explanations. Donny misreads her completely and orders them another round.

Maybe not completely.

On TV, the overtime's turned frantic and the Lakers and Knicks are pouring in the points. Everyone who's watching is rooting against New York, which (she's been given to know) is what all right-minded Ohioans do, no matter the opponent.

"So," she says, "how was band practice?"

He shakes his head. "We're a work in progress," he says. "The singer's why we might be something. Otherwise, the rest of us have our days, I guess."

She inadvertently glances at his missing index finger and then quickly looks away. "Did you come up with a name?"

"We're down to five." He delineates these with the fingers of his left hand. "Gypsy Death. Sunday's Clown. The Alpha-Alphas. Zippo Mission. And Ten Thousand Sludgeworms per Cubic Foot."

She laughs. "Which ones are your idea?"

"The Alpha-Alphas and Zippo Mission. I also came up with Pucker Factor, but today that one bit the dust."

"I like The Alpha-Alphas."

"Thanks," he says. "If I had to bet, though, I'm pretty sure it'll be Sunday's Clown or the sludgeworm one. So how was class?"

"Oh, life-changing," she says.

"Really?" he says.

"No," she says. "Of course not. Class was class."

The jukebox blasts Elvis' "Stranger in My Own Home Town" and segues into Mama Cass' "Make Your Own Kind of Music." The Lakers start to pull away.

She looks at him and, for the first time today, he seems to be looking at her scar. For a moment, she's afraid he's about to say something about it. She's more afraid it will be a compliment. She never knows what to say or do when it's a compliment. He glances away and looks down at his drink and back up at the TV.

But the first compliment: that's when she has to wonder about if or when she'll tell the story and how. She'll never be with any man, she's sure, when there will be a good time to mention the ex-boyfriend, the paring knife from his mama's kitchen, the moment in the wet grass when she thought the worst was over, et cetera. She will never be with any man whose attraction to her does not set problems in motion. Her instinct will always be to flee or to lie, and she hates herself for this.

Again, Donny Sokolove smiles at her and again he looks back down at his drink.

Alice takes a deep breath.

When he turns his head toward her and is about to speak, she reaches over and touches the little dimple in his chin. He doesn't say anything. His skin is soft. Perfectly smooth. Tender, even. He's shaved for her. "Friendly mutton chops," she says.

"What?"

"Your beard," she says, smiling. "I think that's what that kind of beard is called."

He chuckles. "I just call it me being lazy."

Yes. But he shaved for her.

"You want to get out of here?" Alice shouts.

Just as she does, the TV goes black and the music stops cold. For a split-second, she's embarrassed that everyone in Orville's must have heard her.

The bartenders make their hands into megaphones and yell at everyone to settle up—estimate if necessary—and go. The bars are officially closed, *now,* by order of the pigs. Orville's erupts in a conflagration of fury and disbelief. Many of those watching the basketball game hurl their glasses and beer bottles at the TV.

Donny tosses a ten on the bar—surely more than what they owe—and puts an arm around her and (though Alice attributes this to football, not the skills that helped get Donny out of Vietnam nearly intact) somehow cleanly threads their way out of the bar.

The cloud of smoke from Orville's seems to have blanketed Water Street. In its haze, firecrackers are going off and people are chucking rocks and beer bottles and everywhere there's the sound of breaking glass.

Bikers are peeling rubber and getting out of there.

A platoon of town, campus, and county cops advances down the street, abreast, clad in shiny new helmets and shields and other riot gear they must have been thrilled for the chance to use.

Alice sees two terrified women from her three o'clock class, hugging each other and pressed against the wall outside the Ron-de-Vou.

The anger over the order to close the bars has turned a raucous night into something it would have never otherwise become. Whatever that is, Alice can feel it surging through her, something like too many greenies laced with the blow to the heart triggered by a traffic stop.

Alice slams into a man who looks like the stocky man who burned his discharge papers, yells an apology, and is gone in a blur.

Sirens and shrill burglar alarms pierce the din of the crowd.

Down the street, a small bonfire blazes and a young man in a flannel shirt dangles from a traffic light.

People are screaming and swearing and shouting *Sieg heil! Sieg heil!* Some stand their ground, but just as many are hauling ass down alleyways, across parking lots, up the train tracks: whatever it takes to get the fuck out of here.

A blue Ford parts the crowd and careens into a parking meter and a drunk in a suit staggers out, laughing.

Three people get together and throw a manure spreader through the window of the Portage County National Bank.

Donny and Alice are out of there in what feels like ages but is probably mere seconds.

Only after they've made it down an alley and then onto the cool dark of a side street, heading toward campus, do three things click all at once.

First, from the moment they left Orville's until right now, Alice has been murmuring nonstop variations on the word *fuck*.

Second, although the crowd was too thick for them ever to break into a run, Alice is as out of breath as if she'd run a mile full-tilt. Her heart is pounding so hard it hurts.

And, through it all, Donny has been utterly calm and untroubled. He's stayed right beside her the whole time, his hand pressing gently on the small of her back. As this occurs to her, she turns to glance at it.

Immediately, he takes the hand away. It's his left one.

"Sorry," Donny says. In a moment, he's gone from unfazed to awkward. Troubled, even. "I didn't mean that as…I don't know."

As Donny struggles to find the right word, she's afraid he's going to say something like *too forward*.

"Patronizing," he finally says.

She tells him it's OK. It's fine. She gives him a soft kiss on the lips. Alice points down the street and tells him her apartment is just seven blocks that way.

As Donny and Alice make love for the first time, the Commons are deserted and the bell is silent. It's after midnight, which means that the boarded-up ROTC Building will go up in flames later today.

As it does, Ten Thousand Sludgeworms Per Cubic Foot—a band with four members—will perform for three people, Alice among them. Donny, sporting an old Ghoulardi T-shirt and a thrift-store leather vest, will be struggling to keep up with what passes for a beat. The band's barely into its second cacophonous song when an offshoot of the mob that's watching the fire swarms into the Tri-Towers, screaming *Liberate the dance! Liberate the dance!*—only to be deflated by the lack of any dancing or anything worth rebelling against. In short order everyone (Alice and Donny included) will pile outside and chant *Burn, baby, burn!* and try to keep the fire department from saving a building that had some time ago been condemned and scheduled for demolition. By the time the National Guard rolls down Main Street in tanks, the ROTC Building will be nothing but rubble and charred beams.

Sunday will be a better day.

On Sunday, Donny and Alice will be among a group of a hundred or so student volunteers helping the businesses on Water Street clean up the mess and start making repairs.

On Sunday, students and Guardsmen will joke and flirt with one another, and a pretty freshman coed will slip a lilac into the barrel of an M-1 rifle just like the one that will kill her on Monday. The baby-faced Guardsman holding that rifle will blush and keep the flower there, flashing the peace sign as he poses for photographers.

On Sunday, back in Alice's apartment, a basement efficiency with a hippie peace flag painted along the longest wall, Donny will confess that he usually never tells anyone that he was in Vietnam because, often as not, people will spit on him and call him names and women will refuse to go out with him.

On Sunday, he will tell Alice that he is only twenty-one years old. He will tell her that his hand is a long story. He will tell her that he dabbled with the guitar before he went to Vietnam but only got serious about it—if not especially good at it—as a form of physical therapy. He will play for her, just a little bit, along with a Velvet Underground record.

On Sunday, Alice will tell him her scar is a long story too, Donny will accept that. She will take what's left of his index finger and trace her scar with it, and there will be a silence between them and then they will make love again. By then, they'll have lost count how many times. On Sunday, they'll just be two sad people taking an honest shot at being happy.

On Sunday, May 3, Alice and Donny—just like the six students who will die on Monday and the Guardsman who will gun them down, just like pretty much everyone in Kent, Ohio—will go to sleep secure in their belief that, finally, the worst is over.

JAMES JIANG
Diffident Jest: A Look2 Essay on Stevie Smith

In November 1962, Stevie Smith received a letter from "an addict…a desperate Smith-addict." The importunate admirer inquired as to how she might get hold of Smith's elusive first novel (having just completed her own) and hoped to arrange a meeting "over tea or coffee" in London, where she was planning to move in the new year. Smith's reply is gracious though distant; after acknowledging the difficulty of obtaining the now out-of-print novel, she gently pours cold water on the prospect of a rendezvous:

> I do hope your novel goes well & I do hope the move in the New Year goes well too—if only as you suggest, so that we can meet some time.

> I feel awfully lazy most of the time, even the idea of writing a novel makes me feel rather faint! And as for poetry, I am a real humbug, just write it (?) sometimes but practically never read a word. That makes me feel pretty mean spirited when poets like you write such nice letters.

The poet in this case was Sylvia Plath—the newly separated Plath who had, over the course of the previous month, composed the *Ariel* poems; the Plath who would, little over a month into the new year, kill herself in her freezing London flat.

A meeting with Smith, Plath thought, would "cheer [her] on a bit."

Smith was not exactly a cheering poet. Among the many things that she shared with Plath (including: a love of horse-riding, early exposure to the world of publishing, a deft hand at prose) was an abiding awareness of the destructiveness of intimacy, as well as the ability to conjure a sense of despair all the more companionable for its tenacity. Both poets toyed with death in life and art. In the summer of 1953, Smith's severe depression culminated in an attempted suicide. It was in this same period that she produced the single poem on which her posthumous reputation almost entirely stands:

Nobody heard him, the dead man,
But still he lay moaning:
I was much further out than you thought
And not waving but drowning.

Poor chap, he always loved larking
And now he's dead
It must have been too cold for him his heart gave way,
They said.

Oh, no no no, it was too cold always
(Still the dead one lay moaning)
I was much too far out all my life
And not waving but drowning.

"Not Waving But Drowning" shows Smith at her most tragi-comically adept. It is a poem in which the difficulty of distinguishing between depths and shallows is posed by characteristically underpunctuated lines that prove so equivocal to both eye and ear. How are we to read the "no no no" at the beginning of the third stanza? Does the absence of commas make us linger on each "no" longer or does it allow us to skip over them more spryly? Are these the lugubriously self-pitying "no"s of an admonishing spirit (keeping in mind that the collection to which this poem gives its name also includes a poem about "King Hamlet's Ghost")? Or is this the courteous stutter of someone trying to smooth over the simplest of misunderstandings? These delicate ambiguities point to the fallibility of our senses of sight and sound when it comes to detecting the undertow of sorrow.

It takes a peculiar kind of imagination to appreciate the superficial resemblance between waving and drowning—an imagination capable of abstracting itself sufficiently from the drama of a struggle for life to take up an aesthetic interest in gesture and performance. This is not, of course, the same kind of abstraction evinced by the second stanza's anonymous spectators, whose measured diagnosis ("It must have been too cold for him his heart gave way") breaks the measure of the poem, adding an extra beat before the rhythm completely flatlines in the unaccented attribution "They said." The lopsidedness of the lineation and the patness of the "dead" / "said" rhyme create the air of a complacent finality—the dead weight of consensus opinion—that stands for correction in the poem's final verses. Not only is the purported cause of death wrong, but the reports of the man's death may have been greatly exaggerated: he still lies there moaning.

Like Classical tragedy, "Not Waving But Drowning" turns on the relationship between spectacle and suffering, on the presumption that we have at our disposal the adequate means (through speaking and acting) to make our suffering visible to others. But Smith seems to ask if there isn't a kind of *hubris* attached to this notion—if our investment in spectacle (or "larking") isn't more an invitation to continue looking at the mask rather than through it? The poem's "dead man" is too good-natured to deem his onlookers culpable for his fate; however plangent, his "moaning" never sharpens into an accusation. But there lingers a sense that the reader, too, might be complicit in this misrecognition: for couldn't the poem's own blitheness of manner be another instance of "not waving but drowning"? How easily does the heart that gives way give itself away?

Anguish in Smith's work often comes apparelled in the light drapery of fable, nursery rhyme, or ballad. It is this apparent lightness that led early readers and reviewers to compare Smith's work to Edward Lear and Ogden Nash, whose quip "Who or what is Stevie Smith? / Is she woman? Is she myth?" was used to advertise the American edition of her *Selected Poems*. Emily Dickinson and William Blake afford better comparisons. There is more than a touch of Dickinson in "Tender Only to One," an early poem that twists the swoon of petal-plucking sentimentalism into morbidity:

> Tender only to one,
> Last petal's latest breath
> Cries out aloud

> From the icy shroud
> His name, his name is Death.

If light verse is an instrument of sentiment, it is equally a weapon of satire and Smith shares with Blake a temperament of moral severity and wit. Their tactics are also similar. Take the use of the Blakean bestiary in "Reversionary":

> The Lion dishonored bids death come,
> The worm in like hap lingers on.
> The Lion dead, his pride no less,
> The world inherits wormliness.

Or the echo of Blake's "The Human Abstract" in the song of "Childe Rolandine," an adaptation of Robert Browning's "Childe Roland to the Dark Tower Came":

> It is the privilege of the rich
> To waste the time of the poor
> To water with tears in secret
> A tree that grows in secret
> That bears fruit in secret
> That ripened falls to the ground in secret
> And manures the parent tree

Her poems, like Blake's, are more often than not accompanied by images: wiry line drawings of heads, androgynous figures in outlandish costume, animals of the wild and domestic variety, angels and muses both vindictive and salutary, woodlands and suburban scenes. They give her work a children's picture-book quality and occasionally provide a master-clue to the current of feeling in a poem.

In the case of "Brickenden, Hertfordshire," I was, initially, at a loss to explain the pathos and strange power of a poem about a day-tripper's failed quest to find a stream in the wood surrounding a village. The speaker's revulsion is ratcheted up as the quest takes on a nightmarish futility:

I see the pashy ground,
And round and round
My tired feet the rushes twine,
And frogs croak and the sweating slime
Is moved about by an ambiguous brood
Of low and legless life.

It turns out that there isn't a stream after all. Piqued by this failure, the speaker turns on the wood, abhorring its "profligate viridity" as "but a suppuration of earth's humours": "thy sap's virtue comes from dank earth's sweat".

There is something sublime yet childish about the thwarted desire summoned up in this poem and in the recent *Collected Poems & Drawings of Stevie Smith*, "Brickenden" is accompanied by an illustration of a sour-faced child on a hillock of grass. The child has frown lines and a mop of hair resembling a badly poached egg. The relation between text and image isn't immediately clear: Is this intended to deflate the high-flown rhetoric of the poem ("I wept / For the tragedy of unwatered country"), a suggestion on the sly that the speaker's rage is merely a toddler tantrum? Or is there something else at play? The poem's baroque diction seems to rule a child speaker out of the question, but after a while, it dawns on you that the poem is very much about what it means to be a child, about the comfort of origin stories and of knowing one's source. It seems embarrassing to have overlooked what the illustration helps make startlingly clear: that at the emotional core of "Brickenden, Hertfordshire" is a drama of lost and irrecoverable parentage.

The figure of the orphan appears in many guises throughout Smith's oeuvre and one could say (with only a hint of hyperbole) that Smith has been orphaned by the periodizations and groupings by which readers have come to see and understand twentieth-century Anglophone poetry. Born in Hull in 1902, Smith was too young to be a high modernist. Her work first started appearing in the mid-thirties—her first novel, *Novel on Yellow Paper*, was published in 1936; her first book of poems, *A Good Time Was Had By All*, the next year—and it was largely as a "writer of the thirties" that she continued to be thought of (long after "a writer of the thirties" had ceased being a fashionable thing). But she remains an uneasy fit even for that decade with its poetry of political commitment and ideological swagger. Temperamentally, Smith was not a joiner of causes; she was skeptical of "flag-wavers of both sexes," and would chide her friends for the "hubris" of their "world-worrying." In 1942, she could still say: "it is to the poet's merit / To be silent about the war" (compare this to Auden's "maps can really point to places / Where life is evil now: / Nanking. Dachau."). She continued writing poems and novels well into the fifties and sixties, but had little to do with either the macho-nativism of The Movement writers in England (Philip Larkin and Ted Hughes chief among them) or the countercultural energy fueling American confessionalist poetry.

Lack of membership in a clear clique or milieu meant that, throughout her career, Smith had difficulty finding a consistent publisher for her poetry, though she was often in high demand as a reviewer of novels (sometimes at the very monthlies that were turning down her poems). Part of this had to do with the sheer volume of verse she produced and a lack of decisiveness with her own selections; part of it had to do with her insistence that the poems be accompanied by her idiosyncratic drawings. When she did become something of a literary celebrity in the 1960s, it was largely as a result of poetry readings undertaken both in person and on radio. As her biographer, Francis Spalding, observes, Smith's popularity in the sixties is best seen against "a demand for a fresh, imaginative and popular use of language"—a demand that was met in the musical world by the Beatles and Bob Dylan. Working through text, image, and voice, she was one of the first truly multimedia artists.

Smith might best be described as a "problem" poet in the same way that adults will speak of a "problem" child (or literary critics of a "problem" play): problematic because recalcitrant and mercurial. And there was something perennially childlike about her demeanor both on the page and off it. About her everyday life, there was a strange mixture of a fierce independence of spirit and an enfeebling dependency. With an absent father and an incapacitated mother, she lived most of her life under the guardianship of her aunt, Madge Spear (the "Lion of Hull" as she is called in Smith's novels), who coddled her to such an extent that well into middle age Smith had little idea how to boil an egg or open a tin can. At the conclusion of the many literary parties and gatherings she attended in London, she would demand lifts from her friends back to her suburban home at 1 Avondale Road, Palmers Green (about a forty-minute drive out of the city central). Throughout her life, Smith cultivated a "little girl" persona, her signature look consisting of "old-fashioned strap shoes and knitted stockings" and a pinafore over which sprouted the wings of a white shirt collar.

She's in this costume in the widely reproduced photograph of her taken by Jorge Lewinski in 1965. There, Smith is seated at a table, staring off into the top right corner with her mouth slightly ajar as if in mid-thought. What one notices most of all is the tensile strength of her fingers, three of which prop up her head; in the remaining two, a cigarette is wedged. When looking at Smith's illustrations too, I find myself continually drawn to her depiction of fingers. As if belonging to characters out of a Tim Burton fantasy, they are never rounded, but long and sharp, delicate yet deadly.

Returning readers of Smith will be well served by Will May's edition of the *Collected Poems & Drawings*—a scholarly, yet extremely readable volume. But for first-time readers, the best place to start remains Smith's prose. It was, after all, the success of the disarmingly titled *Novel on Yellow Paper* (so-called because Smith's typescript made its way through the offices of Jonathan Cape on yellow copying paper; the New Directions "Revived Modern Classic" edition is printed on paper of the same hue) that launched Smith's career as a poet. Like her two subsequent novels, *Novel on Yellow Paper* is transparently autobiographical, recounting the life and reflections of one Pompey Casmilus, secretary to publishing magnate Sir Phoebus Ullwater (as Smith herself, until her suicide attempt, was secretary-typist to Sir Neville Newnes of the Newnes publishing company). The reader is warned that "this is a foot-off-the-ground novel that came by left hand…if you are a foot-on-the-ground person, this book will be for you a desert of weariness and exasperation." While there is, broadly speaking, a temporal arc as Pompey narrates her life story from birth onward, the novel is more or less a series of digressions on everything from Christian mysticism and the differences between French Neoclassical and Classical Greek tragedy to sex education and the way foreign visitors will use diminutives like "doggie" to impress their English hosts. Equal parts diary, commonplace book, and Beckettian monologue, the book seems narrated by the garrulous love child of Molly Bloom and Tristram Shandy.

Between high and low, bright and somber, Pompey treads a nervy line:

> I am a forward-looking girl and don't stay where I am. 'Left right, Be bright,' as I said in my poem. That's on days when I am one big bounce, and have to go careful then not to be a nuisance. But later I get back to my own philosophical outlook that keeps us all kissable.

In a review that continues to shape Smith's reception, Philip Larkin called her manner "that of the *fausse-naïve*, the 'feminine' doodler or jotter who puts down everything as it strikes her, no matter how silly or tragic." For Larkin, Smith's deeply gendered eccentricity aligned her with modernisms both high and low, with Gertrude Stein on the one hand and Lorelei Lee (the protagonist of Anita Loos' comic novel *Gentlemen Prefer Blondes*) on the other. There is something right about these points of reference (Smith was a great admirer of Loos). But the charge of whimsical indiscriminateness relegates Smith's work to the purgatory of literary spinsterdom in which women writers such as Edith Sitwell, Marianne Moore, Barbara Pym, and Anita Brookner have unfairly found themselves.

I prefer to think of Smith less as an ingénue (*fausse* or not) and more as a jester—if we take jest not in its narrow modern sense of trifle or joke, but rather in its broader etymological sense, as the critic David Bromwich has put it, of a "truth, accommodated to an audience with whom the poet's relation is tactical, but ready for another audience with whom [her] relation may be moral." On this reading, the jester is a sage in disguise, concealing her wisdom behind legerdemain while waiting for the readers and hearers to come along who will see through the act to the plea for recognition. It's no accident that some of Smith's most memorable poems center on the consequences of misrecognition between performer and audience. It's the theme not only of "Not Waving But Drowning," but also of "The Orphan Reformed":

At last the orphan is reformed. Now quite
Alone she goes; now she is right.
Now when she cries, Father, Mother, it is only to please.
Now the people do not mind, now they say she is a mild tease.

The orphan, one might say, is the consummate jester, driven, above all else, by a desire to find and forge a right relation.

In nonfiction, our winner is **Jung Hae Chae** for her story "Pojangmacha People."

Of her essay, nonfiction judge Leslie Jamison said, "A searing lyric built of sweat and salt and sorrow, hot soup and deep shame—an ode to the elderly drunk men seeking solace in the "tiny domed cathedral" of every drinking hut along the highway, and to all the women who have spent their lives caring for them. It's an essay full of pain and grace, both fruits of its uncompromising close attention."

Jung Hae Chae's work has appeared or is forthcoming in *AGNI, Calyx Journal, Crab Orchard Review, Third Coast*, and elsewhere. Her creative nonfiction has been anthologized in the *2019 Pushcart Prize XLIII: Best of the Small Presses.*

When did you first realize you wanted to be a writer?

I don't know that I've ever arrived at such a realization. As long as I can remember, though, I've always had a deep love and respect for words, their sounds and shapes, how they come together sometimes in unexpected ways to mean something very particular, precisely. I grew up with stories and myths, and sometimes miracles happened around me. As a quiet, almost mute, kid who was left alone a lot, I relied on my imagination and those stories, both within and without, to feel less lonely and more grounded. Then, when my family immigrated to the US from South Korea, I gained a whole new language to describe and understand my (troubled) interior, and how it came to be affected by my chaotic exterior reflected in my family's (tangled) history. I felt as though I'd been given this powerful, new lexicon to express my situation, to engage with an audience that wouldn't otherwise have access to such alien landscapes, whether documented or imagined. Like the American Dream, the English language is a language of possibilities, in that its contours are constantly shifting, its borders ever-widening; it's rewarding in the way that a well-earned ending of a poem feels rewarding. Writing in it is both a pleasure and a privilege.

What is your writing process like?

I'm a bit embarrassed to answer this question because if I were being honest, I would say that I lack any process that truly works. Instead, I will say that my process reflects my personality: slow-brewing, detail-mongering, perfection-seeking, but mostly just slow. Everything takes so much time and care, sometimes, most times, unnecessarily. Alas, life.

What inspired "Pojangmacha People"?

"Pojangmacha People" started out as a poem ten years ago when I was working on my MFA in poetry. Its first line, "I'm thinking of the sad old men I knew," had been on the tip of my tongue for a long time before then. After I finally put it down on paper, it soon became a catalyst for recalling all kinds of memories that had been stored away intact in the innermost layer of my gut—*han,* the Korean word for deep lament that defines the soul of the Korean people—that had lived with me my whole life. Pojangmacha, the tiny drinking hut(s) littered along every street corner in South Korea during the 1970s (and even now), this national emblem, became for me a metaphor for depicting the hardened lives borne out by the men and women in my family and the home we left behind. In writing it, I wanted to forgive my own hardness toward the (failed) men in my life and pay tribute to the women who have since passed on—my grandmother and my mother, in particular—the two muses whose sturdy souls haunt me incessantly, but who guide me into the light always. They helped me finish this essay, finally.

Who are you reading? And who informs your work?

I've been weaned on poetry, but lately I've been reading more prose and some memoir as well. I like works that live between poetry and prose, or stories that are told in the language of the subconscious and the otherworld, in verse and/or sentences. Works I have admired deeply and have tried to borrow from include those by Lia Purpura, Cheryl Strayed, Deborah Digges, Jack Gilbert, Paula Bohince, Christine Schutt, Italo Calvino, and of course, the Great Maxine Hong Kingston.

By my nightstand: *Florida* by Christine Schutt, *Educated* by Tara Westover, *Fierce Attachments* by Vivian Gornick, *How I became a North Korean* by Krys Lee, *Air Traffic: A Memoir of Ambition and Manhood in America* by Gregory Pardlo, *Life After Life* by Raymond A. Moody Jr., and *On Earth We're Briefly Gorgeous* by Ocean Vuong.

Do you have any advice for new writers?

As an emerging writer myself, I would say the best advice I was not given, but should have been, is to write into the thing that you're most afraid of. If you're afraid of clichés (in a writerly sense), for example, begin or end your story or poem with a cliché. If you're a grammarian, forget the Oxford comma and write a sloppy sounding sentence. If you're afraid to be sentimental, well, be sentimental. Write a cringe-worthy line, for crying out loud. Break a rule. Or two. Break heart(s). Own it, them. It will free you up to write in the way that feels most authentic to you.

What projects are you working on now? Where is your writing headed?

The current project is guided by my lifelong preoccupation with the women in my family: beginning foremost with my maternal grandmother, the ultimate matriarch of my family made up mostly of women. My manuscript (tentatively titled *Over the Arirang Pass* or *Pojangmacha People*) is a collection of linked essays that centers on the lives of the women (and men) in my family, and delves into facets of Korean history (beginning with the Korean War and its aftermath), as it traverses time and geography, as my family makes its way to America to seek a better life. My work also tangentially explores how culturally differing notions of femininity/masculinity, family structure, of illness, suffering, and trauma translate to socioeconomic outcomes and lived experiences of people across cultures.

While my abiding interest in these issues is rooted firmly in the personal and is based on familial history, it is equally motivated by a desire to unpack the larger historical narratives with respect to how the two Koreas diverged as nations and people (as illuminated by my own family's history), and their places within the context of world history.

  Pojangmacha People

I am thinking of the sad old men I knew. The salt on their drunken foreheads, a sorrow. Of souls stained deep with glutamine and guilt. O, the beauty of MSG. I'm thinking of comfort, the kind rising out of the bodies of blood soups and strangers. Of longing. Inside the tiny drinking tent, the haloed bodies of *haejang-guk*, the mother of all soups, the soup that chased away tremors and trauma and money troubles and time and time and more time, that soup. The bodies. The into-the-wee-hour-drinking bodies, the sitting-with-bottoms-touching-is-just-fine bodies, the bodies sweating out their failing livers, those bodies. Tired and failed as they were, huddled together inside this tiny domed cathedral were their tiny lives, powered by a tiny light, the 1970s-oppressive-cum-underground-guerrilla light, powering the dim city and its people and their small dreams, past the curfew. O, how holy was this light and this coterie, the men lurching headlong into this bloodbath of comfort, the guk chasing away their daily hangovers and bad deeds, only to pass on their karmic debt to their only sons, pass down the bloody mess of their lives. How its biliary notes and fraternal bodies bosomed, not mocked, their chronic bad lives and livers.

My father. I'm thinking of him, but not him. Of souls cursed and caressed inside the *pojangmachas* inside a village. No, not a village but a nation full of sad, sad, old men, with their jaundiced faces riddled with the pock marks of postwar trauma, with their deadly breaths, who lowered their sorry heads into guk after guk, who fawned over their women and children, even as they beat them senseless. The women. I'm thinking of my dead grandmother and my mother, their mothers' mothers, the women gathered at the hair salon next to my grandmother's house, the one with the outhouse. The outhouse. I'm thinking of a childhood lost to dreams, of dreams lost, then found scribbled on the walls of an outhouse, a shit hole brimming with no-good fathers and husbands and lovers, and later of sons.

And the women who made them.

1.

When he drank, only when he drank, my father smeared the brown goo with his bare hands all over the wall next to his bed, the smell so terrible it'd wake everybody up, the women. It was a house full of women without husbands or fathers or keepers. The boorish drunk, the women must have thought, who defied even the worst of their imagination about the war they and their mother have had to endure and the bad men made worse by the war. Torn up by years of drinking, his weak constitution would make him go on the bed prepared specially for him by my grandmother. When he drank, and only when he drank, my father broke through a kind of barricade that he'd self-imposed between himself and the world that had become wholly unpredictable; he was enabled, albeit temporarily, to become just a little more authentically terrible than his usual, more guarded, terrible self.

My father and his father and his father's father all died from an alcohol-induced liver failure in their mid-fifties. While my father was alive, I saw him all of five or six times, and though I couldn't tell whether he was, in fact, intoxicated each time I saw him, he might as well have been, since he was a most sullen human to be around. He cracked a smile not once. His face, a brown jaundiced earth with its deep grooves and cracked furrows, a once-rich gorge now gone dry, would not have tolerated one. He was unpleasant and awkward around people. More precisely, he was reliably capable of inducing the kind of discomfort felt deep in the bellies of people when confronted, say, with a foul-smelling wounded animal in a cage corner, inspiring, at once, empathy and terror. They want to help and free the hurt animal but aren't sure whether he is safe to approach. Picture him brooding silently in an unlit corner of a room with the throng busying themselves on the other side of an imaginary fence, a thin yet impenetrable membrane he was hardly able to cross even under the influence. It may have been that he was incapable of handling all the stimuli—physical, mental, emotional, or whatever other kind—or that he simply didn't care; he'd had enough of other humans. This, all of this, I know to be true, in my own body and mind, because I, too, am often capable of eliciting the same duality of unsafe emotions—of terror and empathy, at once—in those within a striking distance of my anxiety-stricken state. When he drank, only when he drank, he, the wounded animal inside my father, became unleashed from his unlit corner, unafraid to toss around the gooey, brown mess with his forepaws, holding it up to light, in a manner shocking particularly to his women, his preferred audience.

He was known to become violent toward people and animals when he drank. Once, in one of his many drunken stupors, he took a large iron fork, an old rusted tool designed to grab *yeontan*, the cylindrical coal briquettes used to heat homes in South Korea where I grew up in the 1970s, and stabbed his pet dog with it. My brother snatched the almost-dead dog, his beloved dog, and fled the house late at night with it in his arms, in search of a veterinarian neighbor who might save it. The dog didn't survive the night. My brother who was then about ten years old never forgave his father for this misdeed, and this one important bad deed among many scores of bad deeds committed by his father would come to define their relationship—he was his only son. Over time, my brother's hatred for his father grew beyond just him, and defined not only the terms of their relationship but his own sensibilities henceforward toward other people and sentient beings, especially the female kind. With this one stupefying act, our father had ripped open a forgotten wound in the universe, and however small or invisible to the naked consciousness, this generations-defining injury would come to haunt our family. Our father, when he drank, only when he drank, became emboldened to carry out the legacy of misgivings and misfortunes, a carryover from other lifetimes that will, in turn, outlive his and his son's lifetimes.

2.

Spring. I'm thinking of the outskirts of cities, inside the skirts of mothers and grandmothers and great-grandmothers, generations of mothers' mothers. My grandmother. I'm thinking of Sunday mornings. Those early morning screeches of cocks at the hands of the skilled butcher next to the liver shop where my grandmother sent me to fetch her a sliver of the freshest raw pig liver with a dash of sesame oil to help with her eyes. My grandmother, the Man of the House, for all three generations of us women, girl-women.

What I remember are the smells, the complex smells of the open, dirt roads against the tall sky, and the unnamed trees whose branches held softly the metamorphosing bodies of caterpillars that fell to their untimely deaths and landed on unsuspecting passersby beneath them. What I smell is the shit, the complexity of it, from inside the outhouse of my grandmother's house, that lingered after a rain. I feel the tug of the angel whose hands plucked my small body from the abyss, that dark, creature-filled, all-possibilities-filled gaping hole that grabbed at me as I fell into it. I remember the layers of pains of a childhood lost to dreams, in between the layers of myths held untouched and tucked away deep inside her belly.

Inside the giant dome that was the Market, I see the rows of dead fish with their eyes wide open and eyeing back at me as I scurried past them. I hear the shrieks of chickens being picked and primmed and dumped into hot water tanks all in one fell swoop, the cacophony of the black-market vendors haggling or scuffling or cussing or whatever. I see the dirty looks of the old men glaring at my wee-year-old self as I ran away from them. I feel the sweat coming down the foreheads of children, their little hands fastened tight to their mothers', grandmothers', great-grandmothers', aunts', uncles', cousins'. The children, with their honey suckle–soaked finger nails, tiny but beautiful hands of girl-children, of glands of children, packs of eager six-year-olds, chasing each other down muddy streets to the nearest hawker stands, inside the tiny domed tents, to fill their unfillable bellies. There, under a shaky parasol, with their not-as-yet-wide hips, little butts touching, wishing to be touched, they sat and lurched over and into bowlfuls of overspiced rice cakes and fish cakes, into paper conefuls of *beondegi*, roasted silkworm pupa, a perfect after-school snack for growing postwar children.

The rituals. I'm thinking of the rituals, the un-memorable, the un-ceremonious, the un-ritual-est of rituals. Inside the classroom, the prickly-thick clouds up my nostrils, growing like a flooding well, oozing from my lunch or some other kid's lunch buried among all other lunch—a monument or a totem or a mass grave of aluminum lunchboxes—set atop the wood-burning stove that stood in the center of our classroom universe, orbited by seventy hungry children. Didn't matter that the bottom-most always burned to a crisp, a small casualty in this prized communal ritual.

This is what I lived for. Every day, for as many days as there was homework and gym—lunch. And the sharing of lunch. And later, of stories.

This was forty years ago in the capital city of the Republic of South Korea, a place where even seven-year-olds talked politics, whispering to each other during recess who assassinated whom, where they were taught to recognize the propaganda flyers airdropped from the North and sing anticommunist lyrics during morning drills, where midnight curfews made the city's night crawlers scurry to their dens, where the beating of housewives in broad daylight by their drunken-crazed-but-good-hearted husbands was a common spectacle near playgrounds. This was the age of the post-postwar, post-uncles-aunts-first, second, third-cousins-all-living-under-one-roof, post-outhouses, post-orphans and widows left by wars, post-two kinds of Korea. This was the crossroads Korea, the traumatized Korea before K-pop, before Kim Jung Il and his son made the cover of *Time*. This was the alcoholic and liver-failed Korea. This was the Korea that preferred sons, that then raised them to become no-good men, lovers, fathers that passed on too young. The Korea over the *arirang* pass where songs of the beloved rained down on the bridge between this life and the next, as the women waited on their men.

3.

It's the women who told stories. I'm thinking of the women and their seasons. Each autumn, the women from the neighborhood gathered to make *kimchi*, a slow-fermented and deep-spiced cuisine of national pride, not unlike the women who infused them with their own arirang songs of survival. The women would pry open the bok choy, one leaf at a time, and dab the heavily spiced concoction made of salt, garlic, ginger, shrimp, or oyster sauce, onto its thick middle where it sat saturated over days, turning in its own juices, penetrating through the layers of everyday sorrows, surviving through microbes and come-what-may tribulations, long enough to last through the harsh winter. With the opening and closing of each leaf came a refrain and a lyric, of longing: that of good harvest or a husband come home.

I learned about the sorrows of my people, and those of my women, early on. Next to my grandmother's house was a hair salon, a microcosm brimming with yet another kind of longing. This was a small, dirty room tucked away in the back of my neighbor's house, smelling of iodine and perm solution, where I spent all my lazy afternoons listening to the ladies who came to do their hair sit around and talk, just talk. Next to the scissors soaking in alcohol-filled jugs, like a fly stuck on a damp wall, I listened to each woman as she came in and sat in her own chair, to tell her own story or a version of the same story. She—in turn, they—talked about the money they didn't or would never have enough of, and if somehow they could save a little, how they would put the secret stash away, somewhere their husbands wouldn't find it. They talked about the men they dreamed of murdering one day even as they loved them, the men who beat them in front of their children but whom they doted on anyway. If only they were gone, with the money they saved they'd open up a little shop in the burgeoning city nearby and keep all the cash and dye their hair. They complained about the bad sex or no-sex life, about their husbands' mistresses and how they wanted to murder them too. They laughed and laughed out of desperation and despair; they talked and talked about dreams and talked their way into a dream; into the night they talked. It's the stories; they lived through stories, the stories of their own dreaming. They became the stories they told in order to survive. It's the stories their ancestors told and now they told. It's the ancestors who haunted them and now haunt me. It's the women who told stories. I listened, just listened.

4.

My mother left my father shortly after I was born, the third and final child, whose soul fought to live against all the death wishes bestowed upon it. It's the women who wished, whose wishes, if not come true, would spell disorder in the skies. In their estimation, my father, ancestrally drunk, couldn't possibly have anything minuscule to offer my ancestrally beautiful mother, whose immense talent and potential had been sucked out of her by him, a degenerate soul, as far as they could see. None of the savory or unsavory qualities about my father, however, were things I would have known, for a fact, since he didn't raise me. If it were up to him, he would have chosen not to have anything to do with at least two of his children. My sister was the chosen one, his favorite, the gifted one endowed with equal parts earth, metal, fire, water, wood, in her birth chart. During her first birthday celebration, an important marking ritual in which babies "choose" their destined profession, she gravitated toward won, the Korean currency, a sign of her resourcefulness that my father adored. I was his least favorite, the most unlike him and the most like his failed conquest, my mother.

My soul fought to live in order to tell the buried tales of the women, *my* women—mothers without husbands or fathers or keepers, who bore the troubled and drunken-crazed nation on their backs, whose own (her)stories are too complex to tell in a single life time. Sit down, and I'll pour you some *soju*, and serade you with their arirang chants that could be heard at the crossing between this life and the next, about their untold woes still waiting to be told over the arirang pass. Theirs and now mine. Have a listen, just listen.

I'm thinking of trauma. The kind that strikes and lodges at the soul, that is my family and my homeland. I have lived long enough in this lifetime, and perhaps the one before and the one before that, but not long enough to unburden myself of *han*, that generations-defining prefix of suffering that belongs to my people, and to all the women who carried on their backs the men who had gone mad and too frail to take care of their land and lair, let alone their selves. Even in madness, there's a choice; in madness, women dreamed their small dreams, through heartbreaks and seasons, they chanted their arirang songs of survival, of madness. Of han. Why have I been obliged to live by this untranslatable word that is heard only against hard wind, that strikes at my sternum with terror and empathy at once, even as it is sure to fail me? I am singing now because I must, the unfinished lyric of my mother's and her mother's life song over the arirang pass, for I am a child of mothers before I am my father's.

Yes, the trauma. It had lodged unwittingly in the unborn child, as I have come to know. My mother, when she'd become too weakened to have another child, took her pent-up, unspent gall toward her husband, and directed it toward herself while I was growing inside her. When the baby survived, as she took her first breath instead of letting out a joy-cry of exit out of the womb, she exhaled sighs of deep sadness, as if already defeated. When the weakened soul of my mother hovered over her small, frail child, malnourished with bowed legs, she saw that she, too, though lacking in resource, was nonetheless full of lore and light. She left in the middle of the night and took this baby with her.

5

When my grandmother appeared in my dream recently, she brought her young son with her again, the one who had died in his infancy, the first son my grandmother gave birth to as a young bride at age twenty. He's always with her. He was an unadorned soul who had come briefly to test my grandmother's mettle. When he was but a few weeks old, he fell to his death, from a second-floor veranda while my grandmother was tending to my mother, her first-born daughter, whom she would come to resent.

The loss of her first son marked the beginning of her life-long pursuit to do right by her son gods. In 1950, as the Korean War broke out, my grandmother became pregnant with her fifth child, a son. Her husband vanished from the streets of Seoul, presumably kidnapped by the North during a time the North Koreans abducted more than 100,000 South Koreans in an effort to build the newly formed nation of North Korea. It soon became clear that the task of taking care of all four of her children, including the one she was carrying at the time, fell single-handedly to my grandmother. My grandmother—that is to say, women who live through wars and traumas of domestic or national varieties—was a strong one. In those days, strong meant not showing emotion and carrying on about their business, whatever that business was. For my grandmother, this meant taking on sundry jobs for which she had no experience—a (love) letter writer for Korean concubines serving the Japanese businessmen, a seamstress supplying the traditional silken dresses worn by such women, a black-market money dealer, a motel owner, to name a few—all to feed, clothe, and send all four of her children through college. She, like most men and women of her generation, made no secret of the fact that she preferred sons, and would heap all the love and all the resources of the family on that one surviving son, the one she had been carrying at the time her husband disappeared.

My grandmother doted on my uncle, the only man in a house full of women without a father or husband or keepers. At dinners, she served him first, and only the best cut of fish shared by everyone around the table, at a time when even rice was hard to come by. She made sure to praise him for all his gifts, real or imagined, in front of her daughters, some more disposable than others, and instructed them to do the same. As my uncle grew and spoke to her in contempt and demanded material goods from her, instead of denying him, she denied herself. When he married and abandoned his wife and child, she blamed the mother. When he remarried another woman unlike his first wife, and when that wife left him, my grandmother again blamed the mother of his children. When he became despondent, and drank himself to sleep, and as one season folded into another, as my grandmother sang the tunes of her own arirang song, my uncle, the once favorite child of my grandmother and the prize for her son gods, became something of an embarrassment. My grandmother lived into her eighty-eighth year, but had remained vital only until ten years before her death. She had spent the last decade praying to her son gods to restore their faith in her only surviving son, the one who was to carry on the family name, even as it became all but certain that he would die alone and homeless. The last time we heard from him was at my grandmother's deathbed, when he collect-called to ask for money from the family. Even in death, she is watching over him, with her other son in tow. They will watch over him until he joins them there.

6.

I inherited my grandmother's slow ways, her mantra of giving over one's senses to small things intently. The mountains were important to her, as were the birds she became when she danced like a shaman to the shrill-songs of her childhood. I took after, too, her fealty to frail men. When I was five years old, I lived with my grandmother and her grown, unmarried son and daughters, my two aunts and my young uncle, in a traditional Korean home, complete with a courtyard and an outhouse. I loved my grandmother and loved her silence more than anything. The sound of her intense stillness as she worked methodically on small chores taught me to sit quietly with my own longing for my mother. My mother, who had just divorced my father and left her two other children with my father, and me with my grandmother, had been living alone in a one-room apartment and working as a secretary in the big city, hoping that one day soon she could come back to claim all the children once she was able.

My brother, the first-born, was a bright star, the one who was so well-nourished in utero that when he took his first mortal breath, he simply smiled rather than let out a cry of a baby. He, too, longed deeply for my mother, as would a good son gone unnoticed, and would have wished that he was the one she carried in her arms the night she fled my father. Soon after *his* beloved dog died from the injuries my father caused one night, my brother resigned himself to go his own way.

When he showed up at my grandmother's house on December 31, 1975, everyone had laid down to sleep. It was a mid-week and maybe it had snowed that day or maybe it hadn't, but the temperatures were in the minus Celsius and dropping. It must have been my grandmother's voice I woke to, an uncommon thing to hear. She was asking my brother why he had run away, saying that he needed to go back. He had no coat or jacket on. He had no boots or sneakers on, just some flimsy slippers that were coming off his feet. His cheeks were the color of yam's skin. My grandmother's voice was stern and unyielding. I had never heard this sound come out of her before.

By the time I was near enough to my brother to touch him, his legs silken like an icicle, translucent and pink, my heart was already deep in my belly. I was crying but hid it from him, for fear that he would leave me that instant. I thought how oddly beautiful they were, as a rare birthmark is beautiful. I put my small chest, warm from sleep, down whole on his legs and wrapped my arms generously around them, and massaged his hardened toes with my little fingers, careful not to crack them. There, I felt my mortality, as if I could die right then, out of my love for this beleaguered soul, my brother. What was it that I felt but love of a mother, native and awakening in me as if from a deep sleep, that would heal him? I was rooted to the earth and was not scared. I massaged his legs for a while, until I was able to feel the suppleness of his toes, while a prayer sang in my head. Though I was afraid to look up into his eyes, I gazed toward him and uttered these words:

"Oppa, are you here to stay?"

"I don't know." He said like a shy boy.

"Don't leave me. I will take care of you," I said.

7.

When he wasn't drinking, my father was capable of loving and being loved by other humans. When he walked around the house only in his underpants, at all times and without commentary, so as to save time dressing and undressing especially given the trouble with his bowels, he was supremely in his element. When he made up nonsensical words or phrases, strung together with words not easily able to be strung together, to create sounds so ludicrous but sticky and pleasurable to my early ears, he was endearing. When he forced too-tight hugs out of his children and my mother, when he was possessively loving, he was unequivocally human.

The man had an order about him. He liked to start each day with a ritual—a visit to the public bath house. If he got there early enough, he would likely have had the main tub all to himself and been able to control the water temperature as he pleased. He would have likely set it as hot as possible, so as to numb the discomfort he'd have felt from his failing liver. Following the redemptive soak, his next stop would have been a neighborhood corner shack, a modest shop up the street that served the men like my father haejang-guk, spicy hot blood soups loaded with MSG, to chase away the previous night's hangover, only for him to do it all over again later that afternoon. He would have made his way back home, set the radio to his favorite sports channel, then glue himself to reading eight different newspapers to debate state politics with no one. He would've been heard ranting all colorful under his bad breath, in the small, warm, unlit corner of his bedroom, the part of his ancestor-gifted home where he felt least uncomfortable. My father didn't work for a living, and thought working for a living a stupid idea. He liked to play ping pong and eat fish every night. He cooked.

The last time I saw my father was when I visited Korea with my mother one summer, after having left Korea for America a few years earlier. We sat at a restaurant, the three of us. When he spoke to my mother, he didn't look at her but used highfalutin, high register words peppered with what sounded like made-up curse words that were convincing because of his uniquely expressive tone. His whole being seemed like a contradiction in terms, senile but with flashes of radiance. Sad, yet oddly authentic, emotionally. His bizarre behavior made me feel at once kinship and discomfort. When my mother left me alone with him so we could spend a father-daughter time for a short while, neither of us spoke. The only words spoken were on the bus on the way to his house. He had fallen asleep on the bus, and I must have been worried we'd miss our stop. When I tried waking him to ask about our stop, he ignored me. When the bus suddenly stilled to a halt he bolted up from his seat, and flung himself out of the bus, and me along with him.

Once at the house, the silence took over us and calmed us. He was neither curious about me or my mother nor the ways we were adjusting to our life in America. Or, he just wasn't into talking about any of it with me. I was eighteen years old, my buds just beginning to open and giving way toward the sun. I stayed with him for three days and three nights, and each night cooked fish for us, both of us drenched in warm-colored silence as we ate, as if in mourning. The only time our silence was broken was when he hollered from the bathroom out in the courtyard because he needed a clean underwear. He must have soiled at least three that afternoon. Like an obedient wife, I cleaned his soiled underwear, asked for some money to do the groceries, and when he wasn't looking, I primmed up my hair, and spoke very little.

A few summers after that, my father died from falling on the side of a road while walking home alone intoxicated. Though the latter was a routine and the initial injuries he sustained not so severe, because of the delay in getting him to a hospital (he didn't have an ID on him at the time), his brain swelled and he eventually fell into a coma before giving out. He had been living alone at the time, in a house passed down to him by his ancestors, none of whom, dead or alive, would have been proud of what had become of my father. No one was surprised of his passing. According to the women, my father was all but expected to expire much earlier, since his liver had become "paper thin," and that it had been "any day now" for years. He *deserved* to die, they must have thought. There's a saying in Korean, when you die of injuries sustained on the road, your death is likened to that of a dog. My father died a dog's death, alone, without ritual.

8.

Winter. The snow has finally come. Tonight, I'm thinking of the sad old men I knew. Which is to say, the women and the children and the village of my country as I remember them. What I remember are the warmest, unsanitized hands reaching over the hot pot to serve us, all of us. With her back bent, she reaches over the table to serve the neighborhood kids, the latchkeys, the middlings, the good bland kids that looked forward in earnest to those most holy of communions, the portions always wanting, only just enough to come back for more. On those bruised dark days, under the weight of the domed awning, she is there, with the dim lights on, waiting for us. She listens, just listens, to the sad old, no-good men with failing livers, and the women beholden to them, their small dreams tossed out there in the big city. She is reaching, reaching, in eternity, over the arirang pass, to find the lost fathers, husbands, sons, and the village-run-amok-nation, and the women who made them. She looks like my grandmother, but isn't my grandmother. It's the hands of those mothers and grandmothers that had aged, through generations, to serve the men like my father and my uncle and my brother, the sad old men hunched over in rows of pojangmachas, the shabby, late-night drinking tents of the old city, lighting up the dreams and hearts of my people—the men slurring "pour me another one, another one," their low-hum pitch of sighs sounding the night's longing, lost in a place no Google maps will find.

EMERGING WRITER'S CONTEST WINNER
POETRY

In poetry, our winner is **Aurielle Marie** for her poem "a psalm in which i demand a new name for my kindred."

Of her poem, poetry judge Fatimah Asghar said, "The language in this poem is incredibly unique—every line is a slight twist, a turn, a surprise at the end of the breath. The language is just so alive, so right under the skin. This poem instantly captivated me upon reading it and the imagery stayed with me long after."

Aurielle Marie is a Black and queer poet, essayist and social strategist hailing from the Deep South. She writes and speaks urgently about hip-hop, class, race, sex, and politics from a Black feminist lens. She was selected as the 2019 Lambda Literary Poetry Writer-in-Residence. She's received invitations to fellowship from the Lambda Literary Writers Retreat for LGBTQ writers, Tin House, VONA Voices, and the Kopkind Colony. Her poems have been featured in or are forthcoming from the *TriQuarterly*, *The Southeast Review*, *Adroit Journal*, *Black Warrior Review*, and *VINYL*. You can find her essays on Wear Your Voice, NBC, in *Essence*, *Allure*, and *The Guardian*. Follow her: @ YesAurielle

When did you first realize you wanted to be a writer?

I don't know that there was a particular moment I realized I wanted to *be* a writer. I think more honestly, I looked up one day, when I was quite young, to realize that I had taken up writing as a sort-of grief practice. My brother died, and I wrote for him, or, maybe, toward him. My family lost our home, and in the shuttling to stay with cousins or extended family, I never let go of my journals. I was in a writing practice, and it became crucial to my survival. The moment I realized

I *was* a writer, though, that's easy. It began August 9, 2014. The day Michael Brown was murdered by a police officer in Ferguson, MI. I was tweeting and writing essays and poems about the lived experiences of Black youth in America as I organized in our communities. I realized how badly I wanted my writing to pursue a goal beyond my own quiet toiling, and so my poetry and essays began to reflect that charge.

What is your writing process like?

Well, I'm a Sagittarius, so it can be hard sticking to one routine. Instead of forcing more structure, I try to make my spontaneity into a discipline. I bring notepads to bars and coffee shops because my phone will absolutely die at some point, and I don't want to forget conversations I overhear. I scribble on sticky-notes during dates. I spend three hours talking to friends about the rigor of regional ebonics, or African American Vernacular. Then when my head is full, I braindump/purge. Sometimes it barely lasts ten minutes, and other times I crank out five or six different first drafts in one sitting. All of this freedom on the front end is coupled with a pretty rigorous editing process, where I try plugging the drafts into different forms, or using prompts as editing tools, etc. I used to hate editing, but now my free-write to final draft process feels adventurous, which of course I love.

What inspired "a psalm in which i demand a new name for my kindred?"

It's been rewarding to write about the lived experiences of marginalized folks who share my identities. But, I sometimes found myself caught in despair and fatigue as I wrote about trauma and state violence, especially in this political climate. After a particularly hard essay, I stepped back from the work like "Wait a minute, why is all this so sad? I love being Black! I love being queer! I rep the South hard! I need to put the joy back into what I'm writing!" I can't think of a more foundational part of my identity than my community. I have the privilege of being in friendship with some of the most brilliant, magical people I've ever known. I wouldn't be here without them. They deserve all my poems. Throughout the piece, I took care to use language that clarified who my kindred are. Not colleagues, not just friends or lovers, but *my meat, a majestic selfishness, my broke ass friend.* Any reader may be able to guess that my friends are Black and our love is Black, but only my kindred know how I almost drowned at Mozley Park, how I put too much blue grease in my hair, how I was the only one in the waiting room when they went for an abortion. And how magical is it to have written a love poem that is only for them, that is known, too, by the world? *Man, I love them.*

Who are you reading? And who informs your work?

I believe James Baldwin when he said "The duty of the artist is exactly the same as the role of the lover. If I love you, I have to make you conscious of the things you don't see." I'm forever learning from artists who do this in their work. I'm never *not* reading *Poetry for the People* by June Jordan. *Sula* and *Beloved* by Toni Morrison are always close by, as well as her essays on craft. Morrison teaches us so much about the dexterity of language, all its possible iterations, and how to write toward a Black audience with stories that are both *universal* and unmistakably *ours*. Octavia Butler, Zora Neale Hurston, and Alice Walker are writers who I take cues from. Patricia Smith, Terrance Hayes, Kiese Laymon, Camoghne Felix, Tiana Clark, and Ilya Kaminsky too. I think I have to mention that I wouldn't be writing if Danez Smith didn't exist in this world, writing as a queer/genderqueer Black poet with hood slang on the line alongside more "traditional" language. I'm forever grateful to them, and to all these writers, for being models for me.

Do you have any advice for new writers?

The best advice I've gotten is "the best writers are the best readers." Read, read, READ! Additionally, I've heard it said before, that writing is "fearless storytelling." I don't agree. I don't think writing is about being fearless. I think fear is valuable, is an undeniable part of storytelling, especially in marginalized communities. What does it mean, then, to be a writer who acknowledges your fear? Be a writer, humanly fearful, and audacious *despite* it.

What projects are you working on now? Where is your writing headed?

I've (finally!) completed my manuscript *Gumbo Ya Ya*. It attempts to unveil the complexity of Black gxrlhood and Black *queer* gxrlhood, particularly in the South, but it also takes a stab at embodying the page, of positing an intersectionally marginalized identity as the center of the universe, and exploring what it means to be speaking from the middle and not the margins. While working on getting that manuscript out into the world, I'm also working on a collection of essays, on sex and bodies and technology—think, the mood of the movie *Ex Machina*, meets the hit series *Girlfriends*...But like, southern—which I'll be chipping away at while I complete my MFA. I'm also really interested in exploring the rigor and dynamism of Ebonics/AAV, which is to say I want to write in my mother tongue—Southern dialects of creole or Ebonics, and will be investing more of my research and writing in the profound legacy of that, not unlike poetic greats Patricia Smith, and so many others.

a psalm in which i demand a new name for my kindred

after Danez Smith

you caught a bitch in her early nude, paper
thin psalms sharpened into blades on her mother's
lawn, what a mess and you loved her fiercely
not unlike a salvation of noise, your broke ass
hands the arithmetic of Five Points
the library dust in your bones my favorite
poem running over a cliff my dark
bloody muse, my nigga, i love you
in the worst way, i mouth pomegranate
in gummy bliss, kernels falling like manna
into your lap, i milk honeysuckle and your belly
swells with child, you are mine
your youngest born an other
me, your blood pooled beneath his skin, you spit
and we puddle into pink chlorine at Mozley Park
you are my magic, the wicked
Sunday morning song i scythe
from my mother's hair like hot
oil in your kitchen we feast
we commune, bitch you my whole lyric
ain't i said it enough, that you love
like an orange? i pull you from the vine and weep
at how many times you can halve in my
palm and not slip away bitch, you tender
me you give me better language for my
broken you don't pretend to fix i love you
into some better hymn, you the whole soup
you the roux of me, my solemn chew my nigga
you the gristle, i love you the bone splinter
i love you the gum ache, i love you the jigsaw sweat

the deep sigh the belly slick the muscled
sprint from sun to dusk, you the star
i follow to rid myself the Mason Dixon
i line you up over my father's toilet,
when i bleed you gather my family to pray
when i pray you beckon my mother's god
to listen, my god, my best friend i love you,
i love you and am alive
to witness you be this great iteration this majestic
selfishness bitch you give me
my me back, you give me my meat, you give me
enough food to fill my plate my mama
say she got 12 kids and birthed only three
i wish this holy multiplication upon our children
our thick-headed young, a legion of fool ass saints

linked by the hip of their own names
together, long after we dead

In fiction, our winner is **Ruby Todd** for her story "Creation."

Of her story, fiction judge Ottessa Moshfegh said, "This exquisite story about a struggling sculptor was obviously penned by a seasoned conjurer of art and prose. It rings with the truth and precision of memoir, and sings in the peculiarities of magically timed fiction in its feeling and movements. And it is funny."

Todd is a creative arts researcher, teacher and writer of prose and poetry, currently based in Melbourne, Australia. Her work has been published in *Overland*, *TEXT* journal, *Qualitative Inquiry* and *Meniscus*, among other venues, and her fiction has won the Chapter One Prize of the Australasian Association of Writing Programs. She holds a PhD from Deakin University on the subject of elegy, and continues to be interested in the connections between loss and creativity. She is currently working on a novel, and a work of narrative nonfiction.

When did you first realize you wanted to be a writer?

I think when I was around six or seven. I'd always loved being read to, but that was the point when I remember discovering the delight of metaphor, the wonder of language as a tool to capture states of emotion (and then to describe these states to my parents, which was surely equal parts comical and insufferable). The idea of making something, of creating a bright little world in the form of some pages between two covers, also struck me early on as magical. I think I'd always been aware of time as a passing force and as a source of loss, that records such as books might help in some way to redeem, even if only for their author, as in the case of personal diaries. One day at around six years old I decided to "write a book" about Queen Victoria, with whom I was quite taken, perhaps due to our charming Anglophile neighbor who was lovely to me and baked delicious biscuits. I went next door to speak with her for ten minutes as research, and then went home to work on the words and pictures.

What is your writing process like?

I try to write every day, in the morning preferably, as despite not being inclined to cheerfulness at that time, it's when words flow best. Besides, if I write first, I tend to be a more generous and patient person for the rest of the day. My process involves a cup of tea and usually some kind of repetitive minimalist piano music. That might sound pretentious, but I find it helps me access the rhythm and tone of the day before. Beginning a new piece tends to involve probing some element of growing obsession further until it begins to suggest a narrative shape. I've always loved Nabokov's description of feeling a work's generative spark as "the first little throb."

On a broader level, while my process has always been quite intuitive and organic—that trial and error while peering through the dark that many writers discuss—I've lately been experimenting with prolonging the initial ruminative stage before writing the first words of a new piece, and then setting down a kind of skeleton in notes first, which then becomes a kind of constraint, and I've found this to be a fruitful change.

What inspired "Creation"?

"Creation" emerged out of a kind of dialogue with myself about artistic failure, and the question of what such failure costs and, perhaps more interestingly, what artistic success really constitutes. These were questions I myself had been asking before I came to write it, after a difficult period in my writing. The narrator desires for her sculpture some measure of external validation, if only so she might be permitted an audience with whom to share her work, and without whom she senses her creations will never truly live. I think this is a sentiment many artists might relate to having felt at some stage in their creative lives. In the formal struggles and crises of confidence that beset many artists, especially early on and especially in moments when the hallmarks of external success might seem elusive, the question of whether to continue with art and whether it's "worth it" often rears its head. I've noticed that at such times, art can begin to feel like an absurd compulsion, a kind of self-cannibalism or replacement of real life that might constitute a form of madness. To me this felt like an interesting and perhaps cathartic kind of test to explore in a story, because such moments in my own life have ultimately always served to clarify my commitment to the work itself. Such moments have for me, as for the narrator, also served to make me question in fruitful ways what authoring a work really entails, what it means to be haunted by the creations of earlier artists, and how to ultimately find and make space for your own voice.

On a simpler note, I've always had ekphrastic tendencies and love writing about visual art, and found myself writing "Creation" at the tail end of a long project, which also had sculpture as one of its subjects.

Who are you reading? And who informs your work?

I just finished reading Sarah Manguso's intimate meditation on diary writing, *Ongoingness: The End of a Diary*, and appreciated her explorations of the connections between writing and the losses of time. I also recently completed the final installment of Rachel Cusk's wonderful Outline trilogy, and am still struck by the immersiveness of its atmosphere, and by how widely the narrative ranged while holding the reader within the sound of its singular, dry-witted voice. I'm now halfway through Jeremy Reed's biography of the fascinating English writer, Anna Kavan, *A Stranger on Earth*, who is a new discovery for me.

Some of the writers who continue to inspire me include John Banville, Vladimir Nabokov, Marilynne Robinson, Marguerite Duras, W. G. Sebald, Wallace Stegner, Anne Carson, Jeffrey Eugenides, Daphne du Maurier, Patricia Highsmith, and Elizabeth Smart.

Do you have any advice for new writers?

I'm not sure I have any advice to offer that's very new; what occurs to me has been said many times before—read and write, keep going, and write because the writing is first its own reward as there's no guarantee you'll be able to make a career of it. I think something I wish I'd been told years ago is that, despite the standard adages, just because you identify as a literary writer doesn't mean some degree of advance planning is somehow incommensurate with the form and style you work in. I think many writers who don't plan to some degree in advance might assume it's the most authentic method generally, in terms of inviting unconscious influence into the early stages, but also underestimate their own deftness for structuring and plotting along the way. Because I tend to be quite detail-oriented, and focus on building a narrative on the level of small images and immediate, individual moments in time, I've found recently that approaching a long-form project with a more distinct stage of pressing out the lineaments of an outline—which I can then work within on that more micro level, even as the wider shape shifts and continues to surprise me—is quite freeing.

What projects are you working on now? Where is your writing headed?

I'm currently in the midst of writing an oddball psychological thriller with astronomical themes, set between the US and Australia at the turn of the last millennium, while also revising a completed novel manuscript. I'm also working on a manuscript of narrative nonfiction that explores some of the themes of my previous doctoral work in a more open-ended and playful way, relating to the different ways we navigate the limit that death, and other more contingent kinds of loss, represents for the living, especially in the context of our present climate and ecological emergencies.

Creation

1

Decades ago at the start of a Melbourne autumn, my friend Sara invited me to a party. I don't like parties—she knew this—yet still I heard her bright expectation on the other end of the phone. I'd been watching the street darken through the window when she called, and as she waited I lurched around silently for an excuse that didn't sound like a lie. "We'll have to go shopping for outfits," she said when I finally agreed to go, as though this would be part of the fun.

Back then I was working in an office that smelled of old carpet, as a secretary for an Ear, Throat, and Nose doctor whose orders, issued in a thin, pained voice, echoed in my mind when I wasn't there. I often wished I'd had the foresight to train for another profession—something unassuming yet autonomous, like archiving or copyediting. But in quiet moments, it was the life of the nuns in the brick building opposite mine that I longed for, the building's blinds always drawn like eyelids against the day.

In my real work as an artist, I seemed to be failing, but couldn't have stopped my sculpting if I tried, which somehow made the failure worse. As if to punish myself, I filed each piece away in plain sight on my long workbench under the window that looked out at the nunnery. My creations would eye me as I drank tea in the mornings, an audience at once indifferent and resentful. At other times, they would form a kind of company and look out with me at the neat figures of nuns on the grounds, whose heads always seemed inclined toward each other in serene conspiracy. How wonderful, I would think, to believe in a creator being to whom we all returned.

At ever-increasing intervals, I would attend shows by friends from art school whose work had met with some measure of success, and eat cheese with them. I would wonder whether they believed I had attended in order to benefit from their connections, and wish that feeling pleased for them were not such an effort. Then I would stay up late, warring with a block of clay to focus my attention to its stillest point, pressing out the contours of some face I had seen or dreamed, hoping it would prove the exception to the disinterest my work had elicited from gallerists and dealers in town.

While the face or figure was still emerging under my thumbs, everything would feel possible, as if I were solving the final alchemical riddle. Some afternoons, the living force of the clay seemed to fill my blood with light, at other times it felt like a kind of birth. Even if the result was disappointing, I had the labor—more and more, I saw that this was what I lived for. But my hope was brazen; each block I cut lifted my sails for a few days. To preserve this feeling, I would sometimes abandon a work while its features were just appearing. Yet these abandoned works, too, were disappointing, as if without the warmth of my moving hands keeping their fate mobile and pointed toward the future, the promise that once had been visible died. This death was more devastating when I carried a work to the final stage: it emerged into the room with me, open-eyed; we looked at each other and I saw not only that it was dead but also that it had never lived. I would lay it to rest alongside the other half-dreams and register in my body another kilo of phantom weight. Then I would wish not for success but to relinquish the desire for an audience, which shadowed truer things. I would see some awful story on the news—a mudslide in Bangladesh, or a child murdered by a man with lizard eyes—and recognize my absurdity.

On the Saturday before the party, I met Sara at Myer. I trotted behind her like a lady-in-waiting, bundling dresses under my arms. I remember finding the colors of that season too bright, the fabrics too harsh, the shapes too boxy. Sara tried on dozens of dresses, squinting at her reflection and then at me with desperate seriousness, and sighed when I suggested they were all quite nice. Bored and longing for an ice cream from the cafeteria, I suggested she try on a simple crepe tea dress I had noticed hanging on the returns rack, in a mulberry color, which would suit her pale skin. She only plucked at the fabric with a scowl when she tried it on, finding it tight at the bust and too plain.

"Give it to me," I said finally, trying to hide my frustration and aware that owing to wearing only pajamas at home and avoiding outings like these, I, too, needed something new.

She raised her eyebrows when I stepped out of the change room. We peered at my reflection in the mirror as I turned around, looking for a weak seam or misplaced dart. The dress enclosed me as if a tailor had measured it. My face in the mirror looked more vital somehow, as if it knew something my real self would discover only if I bought the dress.

"I think this will do," I said, feeling a strange heat on my chest just under the sweetheart neckline.

At the register, I asked the sales assistant to remove the tag of the dress while I was still wearing it. After saying goodbye to Sara, I walked along the river in a daze, arriving home only to descend into a dreamless sleep.

2

I woke with the sun, posed as I had collapsed the day before, straight as a mummy with a strange tingling on my skin. I showered and put the dress back on. In the mirror I peered at my face and wondered whether the pink in my cheeks foretold good health or a coming fever. Standing in front of my workbench under the window, I looked outside in the avenue at the plane trees, which seemed to have turned yellow overnight. I looked at my languishing clay creatures and was surprised to feel no weight of sorrow or dread. With less forethought than usual I sat down, sliced a block from the terracotta slab, and descended into the strange half-sleep of making, in which my fingertips took on the function of sight.

Usually I had an idea in mind—a boy I had seen on the bus with a wistful expression, or a woman at the supermarket with a marvelous number of chins. Sometimes I would flesh out figures at speed to see if I could lose some of the stylistic preciousness of which I had been accused. I imagined finding a brand of economy as elegant as Giacometti's attenuated forms, or as satisfying as Paleolithic artifacts with their strange, lumpen poise. But I would pause and second-guess my hands, and my speed figures would look confused and overwrought, as if to spite me. Regardless of my efforts, every work I made betrayed my love of the Roman bust: fine detail, correct proportions, earnest gazes. I had perfected hair in a series based on *Flavian Woman*, for which my mother sat for hours in a wig while watching reruns of *Prisoner*. I would listen to entire classical albums while erasing evidence of my fingers with alcohol and fine brushes. I ruined a lot of work this way.

That Sunday, it was as if the nerves of my hands worked apart from me, while my eyes paused for long moments on the plane trees outside, observing the emerging shape only from a blurred distance. With an empty mind, I enjoyed the slippery coolness of yielding clay, its loamy smell of earth quarried somewhere far away in France. When at last I paused and focused my eyes, I saw a woman's face looking at me with careful attention. It took a while to register my surprise, as I felt I'd been dreaming. She was middle-aged, with a high forehead and strong nose. She seemed to have a shock of wiry hair swept back. I noted that my lack of conscious attention in sculpting her had led to a swift, mobile confidence of form that was never a feature of my careful, methodical style. I stepped back from the face, and peered at it from a distance as I made coffee. I half expected her expression to have changed when I returned, but it was the same: a measured expression of the mouth that might precede a realization, or smile. "Who are you?" I asked. I was enjoying the feeling of surprise, even if it was of an unnerving kind.

I felt as if I were overheating, and left to walk a few blocks for fresh air. When I returned she was the same as before, and I considered that perhaps I had awoken in a strange mood that was affecting my judgment. I ate a sandwich, thinking food would steady me, and took a painkiller as I had a headache. Eventually, I sat back down. As if we were being watched I affected an air of disinterest toward the face, and without meeting her gaze, deposited her at the end of the line of other faces.

I cut another block. *La Traviata* began playing on the radio, which somehow quelled the atmosphere of expectation. I began with slow deliberation: I would model my father's face. It was only once I had marked out his eye sockets and cheekbones that I began to relax, recognizing them as correct, feeling the music fill my chest. After a while, I opened the window to let in a breeze. By now I was smoothing out the eyelids, finding myself looking out the window again. Finally, I registered that my attention had strayed, and jolted. It wasn't usual for me to grow so distracted while sculpting. I looked back at the emerging face, and felt a cold heat begin to spread. I was no longer looking at my father. The face had become strange, the face of someone I'd never seen. He was about the age of my father, but there the resemblance ended. His fascia was craggy, his cheeks sunken, his brow bone pronounced. I sensed he would have a sharp, clever gaze when I fixed his pupils.

I wondered whether I was hallucinating. I set the man's bust by the woman's, to the far side of the table where I had to strain to see them. I draped them both with cheesecloth and then fitted each with a plastic bag to ensure an even dry. I wondered whether to destroy them. I was frightened of looking away, in case their faces continued to develop and change without me and I'd have further cause to doubt my own mind. The light was fading now. Exhausted, I went to bed.

The next day, I attended work in a fog. Dr. Heiss had back-to-back bookings all day.

"You look flushed," he said without expression when I set down his coffee. His observation didn't seem to require an answer as he had already returned his gaze to his appointment schedule. I said nothing, and detoured to the bathroom on my way back down the hall. I couldn't tell if my face was flushed as the light was unnaturally yellow, but I did look mildly stunned.

The day's appointments rolled by: a deviated septum, an ear infection, chronic sinusitis. At the desk in between patients I worried the rash on my chest was beginning to welt under my blouse. I wondered whether it was allergies, and whether I would have to miss the party after all.

At midday, Mr. Rodriguez appeared for his tonsillectomy. As I looked up and smiled and started greeting him in the usual way, I felt as though my mouth was suddenly moving apart from my brain, as shock dawned and I checked his features to disprove the impossible fact that his was the face my blind fingers had made the afternoon before. He didn't seem to notice my conflict. He clutched a sheaf of papers, smiled cautiously, and bit his lip. No one looked forward to appointments with Dr. Heiss. As Mr. Rodriguez read the paper in the waiting room, I tried to convince myself that I had conjured his face because I had seen him before in passing, even if I had never summoned his face consciously since. I checked the appointment book to find the date of his initial consultation, January 4th, and felt somewhat better.

I had lunch at a café, watching the stream of people on the sunlit street instead of thinking about Mr. Rodriguez, and wiping my nose with serviettes. My eyes were itchy, the light too bright. I wanted to go home and draw the blinds.

On Friday, I called in sick. In the dim morning, I sat by the window, short of breath with blocked sinuses, although the rash on my chest seemed to be healing. The flat had a furtive feeling, as if I'd caught it out in its expectations for a day without me in it. My eyes slid over the row of heads, arrested and disembodied like the remnants of some small-time dictator's genocide.

I was a comparatively lazy sculptor, preferring the ease and immediacy of working from a solid block that I'd then hollow out. I didn't like the calculated beginnings of the cylinder technique, and whenever I used an armature, I was always too anxious to ensure the resulting work validated the effort of screwing a flange and board and scrunching up all that newspaper. Although I dreamed of one day mastering bronze and iron casting, I loved the immediacy of clay, its earthen smell, the sense of my own body wrestling another into being. I low-fired the ones I liked and used patinas, oxides, and resins to create a look of age. At that time, I was experimenting with black oxides to mimic iron, and had begun to paint the eyes in the Roman style. But I needed a trademark, a shtick. Many successful contemporary sculptors of a classical bent seemed obsessed with mythology and monsters. Medusas, hermaphrodites, chimeras, and grinning things with horns all seemed to do well, reconnecting the public with the tradition of Etruscan monsters in work that was often far less sophisticated than the originals they were inspired by. But art rarely responds to reverse engineering for the market, and the market didn't need any more technically proficient Medusas. I could think of few alternatives, seeming to lack the gift of narrative invention. I wondered whether this meant I was a craftswoman rather than an artist.

Because I hadn't bothered firing or casting or making a mold of anything for months, some of the heads I'd left uncovered had begun to crack. I imagined hurling them all through the window to shatter on the road, so that when the nuns went out to buy milk they would have to step over noses and ears and bits of skull. I tried to imagine it, but couldn't decide whether they would be horrified or amused. I wanted to believe they'd be at least intrigued, and glance up at my window with wondering expressions.

Looking at the heads, I questioned whether there were any worth firing at the community kiln studio. I walked over to the two new heads and lifted their coverings. I peered at Mr. Rodriguez, for it was indeed him, and at the wire-haired woman, those faces that seemed to have appeared without my intervention a few days before. I touched a hand to the woman's cheek, and figured she was dry enough. I decided to fire her, if only so I could reassert control over the strange way my practice had run away from me, and so that I could try a new satin-hard glaze.

As I walked through the park that led to the studio, carrying the head in a padded hatbox, I began to feel hopeful. Perhaps this head would be a success. Yet it was difficult to feel attached to a work that didn't seem to have required me for its existence. There was a bench outside the studio, and as I passed it I wished I could just sit there in the dappled light instead, without ambition or concern for the future.

The surly attendant didn't look up when I entered. She was instructing a woman with coiffured hair and peacock earrings on how to operate one of the potter's wheels, guiding her hands as they laughed. I had never seen her so animated. I signed in and took the hatbox over to the bench by the kilns where I pulled out the head and rested it on the bench in its wrappings.

Eventually, the attendant came over. "Here for the firing?"

I nodded.

"OK, get it ready to put in." She gestured to the head before stalking over to the kiln and fiddling with the trays.

"Only just bone dry," she said when I handed it to her, regarding me with the muted look I imagined she reserved for most artistic frauds. Then, for some reason just as she was about to set the head down, she looked at it—something she never did—and then looked at me.

"Was this modeled from life?" she asked, frowning with real curiosity.

"No," I said, puzzled, and asked what she meant.

"It's Cynthia Lerner, isn't it?"

She sighed when she saw my blank expression.

"The sculptor. She did the bog series? Anyway, she died a few weeks ago. This is the spitting image of her."

I wasn't able to speak. After leaving the head with the attendant, I sat in the café next door, looking into my coffee and feeling dizzy.

3

Instead of planning the colors for the glaze that evening, I went to the library. I worked through the previous fortnight's newspaper obituaries until I found Cynthia Lerner's, alongside the thumbnail photo I'd been hoping for. It took my tired eyes a moment to adjust. Then, there she was; the image of Cynthia Lerner and the image of the clay face I had made, converging as I stared, like a death mask over its model. I wondered what it all meant. Unlike Mr. Rodriguez, I was certain I had never seen Cynthia Lerner before. A librarian helped me to find an old catalog of her work, and as I flipped through its pages, I realized that the style in which I'd made the last two heads was her style. I squinted at the catalog images and saw the same swiftness of form, the same half-finished features. Lerner was a master of suggestion. She knew when to stop. Her figures and busts seemed always to still be emerging from, if not trapped in, the clay they were formed from. You could see the tracks of her fingers and thumbs—faces and limbs were formed from smears and divots, a thick, roiling surface. Her most famous work, for which she had won the National Sculpture Award, was a series of prostrate figures in bronze, based on the bodies found throughout the centuries in the bogs of Northern Europe: Tollund Man, Grauballe Man, Lindow Man, Yde Girl. I'd marveled at photographs of those bodies myself, appearing as they did like readymade sculptures, their burnished peat-preserved skin softened and wrinkled like overworked clay. In 1950, Tollund Man's head emerged from the bog separate from his body, wearing a pointed sheepskin cap and the noose used to kill him in the Iron Age. Otherwise, he looked like a man asleep, with beard stubble and the wrinkles of late middle age. Lerner didn't try to replicate the forensic detail of these real bodies. Instead, her bodies looked as the originals might have while still covered in peat, before archaeologists had revealed the finer details of their flesh.

On Saturday, I collected Cynthia's head from the studio and glazed it in a conscious imitation of her mature style, using a green oxide wash to imitate bronze. When it was finished, I took it to one of the better galleries in town, run by a man I had attempted to see many times and whom I had begun to imagine as a shadowed, imperial figure like the perpetually absent masters of old European estates, whose names haunted their houses and servants. One of his artists made Plasticine figurines of monstrous humanoid figures variously eating, fucking, or giving birth to each other. Another made silkscreens of his Scottish Terrier superimposed against backdrops by old masters—Velázquez, Bosch, Titian—while ripping off the style of Warhol's *Marilyn Diptych* shamelessly. Both were hits at home and overseas. In my darker moments I imagined them all colluding in some art-world version of the Knights Templar.

Once I had scanned most of the back catalogs and drunk too much water from the cooler, the receptionist informed me that the gallerist's assistant would see me. Eventually, he ambled out from his office into the reception area, a bearded Irishman in a lime green shirt. In his office, like a supplicant after many failed harvests, I handed him the head in its box. Without expression he peered in, drew it out and looked it over, while I observed an abundant vase of yellow tulips that were just beginning to turn.

"Lerner, isn't it," he said, in the same expressionless manner. "A portrait—and an homage to her style." He looked at me with narrowed eyes. "OK," he shrugged. "Send photos of more work."

He reached out his hand for me to shake, and that appeared to be the end of it. I wasn't sure what to feel.

Walking home, I realized that the portrait of Lerner was a trick I could play only once. Simply imitating another artist's style over and over across a variety of different subjects, without variation or irony or critique, was the realm of plagiaristic kitsch. Even if I could, I did not want to sell souvenirs. Yet none of my previous work was suitable to photograph. Somehow I needed to make more work in a style consistent with the previous two heads, the style of Lerner. Each evening for the following week, I sat down to work, invited the strange trance out of which those two heads had emerged, and then proceeded to make work in my own dependable, unsellable style.

By the next Saturday, the day of the party, I was exhausted. Only my affection for Sara propelled me there, wearing the dress and a far too cheerful shade of lipstick. All my remaining energy was spent pretending I was enjoying the crush of people and their banshee sounds, the bludgeoning music, and the flavorless fried food that was meant to justify the price of the ticket, for which I could have bought a good number of oxides and Mason stains. Eventually, just after midnight when a nice-looking man and his friend got talking to us and I could see that Sara was deep in a mutually enjoyable conversation, I was able to kiss her goodbye and leave with a good conscience.

Back home, I felt strangely awake. Looking out at the dark street, I had the idea of staying up to see the dawn. To pass the time, I thought I'd try to make another head. After my recent failures, I had no expectation of creating another Lerner. Then, having spent an hour or so roughing out the main features, I realized I'd been looking for a while at the lights of the nunnery while my hands had kept moving. Looking down, I saw the emerging face of a young girl smiling, made in the style of Lerner. Finally, I asked myself what conditions in that moment were the same as they had been last time, and it occurred to me that it was the dress. In front of the mirror I removed my art smock and pulled the dress from my shoulders. Peering at my chest, I saw that the redness followed the faint line of the sweetheart neckline. It didn't make sense. I couldn't fathom the apparent connections between my sculpting, a dead artist, and an allergic reaction to fabric.

Every night for the next week, I wore the dress as my nose ran and my chest welted. I made bust after bust in Lerner's style from a cylinder base. It was almost mindless, a trick my body knew when wearing the dress. I built up a cache of them over days, like bullets to be deployed. When I realized I had enough, I took off the dress and eyed the busts for hours in the comfort of my pajamas, wondering how to make them my own.

For several nights as I recovered from my symptoms, I couldn't sleep. I would doze off and find myself in Surrealist nightmares—among giant marble heads in shadowed public squares; being chased by Gorgons in ruined cities. On one of these nights, I rose from bed, walked through the half-light to my workbench, and picked up a wire-ended tool. I lifted the plastic from one of the busts, a well-formed young man whose head was downturned in thought, his mouth suggesting a smile. Squinting and quick in an effort to beat thought, in a single motion I sliced the head in half. The right side fell onto the bench, leaving the left still attached to the base. The wire loop left a deep uneven gouge on the side that still stood, exposing the head's hollow interior. There was something austere and satisfying about this deconstruction. I felt something lift in me as I looked at it. I tried the same technique on another head, this time cleaving away each side so that just the middle section was left. I realized that I could reveal this negative space in an infinite number of ways. I could break the heads after firing and reassemble them with missing parts. I could mount sections of their faces on walls, to create the simultaneous suggestion of appearance and disappearance. I could create an installation of fragments.

A month later, the gallerist's assistant agreed to include one of the shattered heads in an upcoming emerging-artists' show.

I didn't wear the dress again, but neither did I discard it. It hangs in my wardrobe still, a reminder of something uncertain.

John C. Zacharis First Book Award

photo by Ye Rin Mok

Ploughshares is pleased to present **Xuan Juliana Wang** with the twenty-ninth annual John C. Zacharis First Book Award for her collection, *Home Remedies* (Hogarth, 2019). The $1,500 award, which is named after Emerson College's former president, honors the best debut book by a Ploughshares writer, alternating annually between poetry and fiction.

This year's judge was Ladette Randolph, Ploughshares' Editor-in-chief. About the book, Randolph wrote: "*Home Remedies* brings together a wildly diverse group of stories, each of them a glimpse into contemporary Chinese culture and the ways it moves between the US and the Chinese mainland. Wang takes big risks in this collection, and in story after story those risks pay off in surprising ways: bold structural innovations; wide-ranging moods from comic to meditative to tragic; and subjects as varied as traditional Chinese tales, immigrant stories, the confessions of decadent, neglected youth, and stories of disillusionment and hope. *Home Remedies* is only the first achievement by a major literary talent."

Xuan Juliana Wang was born in Heilongjiang, China, and moved to Los Angeles when she was seven years old. She was a Wallace Stegner Fellow at Stanford University and received her MFA from Columbia University. Her work has appeared in *The Atlantic*, *Ploughshares*, *The Best American Nonrequired Reading* and the Pushcart Prize Anthology. She lives in California.

What inspired *Home Remedies*?

Los Angeles, Beijing, and New York. Art galleries, architecture lectures, and a computer science course. Nan Goldin, Ren Hang, and Ryan McGinley. Jean-Luc Godard, Björk, and Woody Allen. Lou Ye, Jia Zhangke, and Wong Kar-wai.

What did you discover or grapple with while writing the book?

It took the entire span of my twenties to write this book. During this time, I lost some of my powers and gained new ones.

How does this book fit with the rest of your work?

These are the stories I've been aching to tell all my life: about my history, where I come from, where I've been. There was something on the line for me in all of these stories, and I hope—I can already feel it happening—that with this first book something in me will have shifted. After this I'll be new.

What kind of research do you do, and how long do you spend researching before writing?

I am always taking notes for a story. I like to describe rooms, mustaches, something funny someone said, certain mannerisms of cats, and write them down on ticket stubs, airsick bags, and napkins. Then once in a while I'll type them up into passages and some of that will usually end up in a story. I tend to do more conventional "research" after most of the general arch of the narrative is already written.

What are you working on now?

I'm working on a novel and some memoir pieces. I am writing love stories of the new Chinese diaspora, paying homage to contemporary Chinese photography, and growing up.

Book Recommendations from Our Former Guest Editors

Tess Gallagher recommends *To the Wren: Collected & New Poems 1991–2019* by Jane Mead (Alice James Books, 2019). "This book collecting all of Jane's work from 1991 to 2019 arrives as we look to celebrate this incomparable writer's tough-tender true-hearted way of singularly bringing into language ways of being with each other. There is just nobody like her, writing as if language was just being minted as she wrote out of her searching mind and heart."

Rigoberto González recommends *The Boy in the Labyrinth* by Oliver de la Paz (The University of Akron Press, 2019). "A touching long poem from a father to a child with autism. The range of emotions mirrors the range of poetic forms, a journey with no end or reconciliation, yet all of it an expression of love."

Joyce Peseroff recommends *Persephone Blues* by Oksana Lutsyshyna (Arrowsmith Press, 2019). "Lutsyshyna's witness includes wars both within and without: 'eastern Europe is a pit of death and decaying plums / I hide from it in the body of America,' even while America sings 'her silent highways / her pointed southern gothic / her flies that hover over the bodies of the dead.' Passionate and luminous, her poems answer a roommate who asks, 'native language, / what's it for you?' with 'It's a house with no room for darkness.'"

Robert Pinsky recommends *My German Dictionary* by Katherine Hollander (The Waywiser Press, 2019). "A magnificent first book of poetry, selected for publication by Charles Wright, who accurately calls these poems 'wise and brave.' A lexicon of grief, this book has the emotional, historical force of *knowledge*: knowledge of language and of languages, with their unknowable measures of horror and redemption."

Lloyd Schwartz recommends *Because What Else Could I Do* by Martha Collins (University of Pittsburgh Press, 2019). "This is a devastating and hauntingly beautiful book about a tragedy that leaves you grateful for poetry as a medium of expressing and sharing grief."

Lloyd Schwartz recommends Jill McDonough's *Here All Night* (Alice James Books, 2019). "I love Jill McDonough's poems because they make me laugh and cry at the same time. This is a wonderful book and her poem 'Cindy Comes to Hear Me Read,' about a former prisoner and how she spends her new freedom, is just by itself worth the price of the book."

Richard Tillinghast recommends two rereads: *Postcards* by Annie Proulx (HarperCollins, 1992), and *Housekeeping* by Marilynne Robinson (Farrar, Straus and Giroux, 1980). "I like to revisit classics, and these are two of the best books of our era. Both are dark. Both tell of the disintegration of American families. *Postcards* gives a panorama of America from the thirties to the present; *Housekeeping* is an extraordinary critique of domesticity and the coherence of the family unit."

EDITORS' CORNER

Robert Pinsky, *The Mind Has Cliffs of Fall: Poetry at the Extremes of Feeling* (W. W. Norton & Company, October 2019).

Edward Hirsch, *Stranger by Night* (Knopf, February 2020).

CONTRIBUTORS' NOTES

Erin Adair-Hodges is the author of *Let's All Die Happy,* winner of the Agnes Lynch Starrett Poetry Prize (University of Pittsburgh Press, 2017). A Bread Loaf-Rona Jaffe Foundation Scholar in Poetry, Sewanee-Claudia Emerson scholar, and winner of *The Sewanee Review's* Allen Tate Prize and the Loraine Williams Prize from *The Georgia Review,* her work can be seen in journals such as *The Kenyon Review, Boulevard,* and *Prairie Schooner.* She is an assistant professor of creative writing at the University of Central Missouri and is the coeditor for *Pleiades.*

Janan Alexandra is a Lebanese-American poet and MFA candidate at Indiana University. She is the recipient of fellowships from the Martha's Vineyard Institute for Creative Writing, the Provincetown Fine Arts Work Center, and the Bucknell Seminar for Younger Poets. Janan has taught creative writing to youth for several years and currently works as Associate Director of the Iowa University Writers' Conference. You can find her work in *The Adroit Journal, Mizna: Prose, Poetry and Art Exploring Arab-America, Cosmonauts Avenue,* and elsewhere.

Beulah Amsterdam grew up in the Bronx on welfare. She worked as a waitress, clerk, telephone operator, dental assistant, and psychiatric technician on her way to becoming a clinical psychologist. She has published poetry in her chapbooks, *Black Frogs That Fly* and *Visit,* as well as in various journals. Her memoir stories have appeared in *Voices: The Art and Science of Psychotherapy*, *Gravel*, and *Dime Show Review*. She lives in Davis, Calif.

Nick Arvin's most recent novel is *Mad Boy* (Europa Editions, 2018). His writing has appeared in *The New Yorker*, *The New York Times*, *McSweeney's Quarterly*, and elsewhere. His story "The Crying Man" won Ploughshares' 2014 Alice Hoffman Prize for Fiction. He is also an engineer, living in Denver.

Ferenc Barnás is one of Hungary's most distinguished writers. He is the author of five novels. *The Ninth* (Northwestern University Press, 2009) was long-listed for the Best Translated Book Award (USA) and the International IMPAC Dublin Literary Award. His fourth novel, *Another Death* won Book of the Year in Hungary, the Aegon Award. He has received three of Hungary's highest literary honors. His works have been translated into German, Serbian, and Indonesian. He currently lives in Jakarta, Indonesia.

Malachi Black is the author of *Storm Toward Morning* (Copper Canyon Press, 2014), a finalist for the Poetry Society of America's Norma Farber First Book Award and a selection for the PSA's New American Poets Series (chosen by Ilya Kaminsky). Black is a 2019 NEA Creative Writing Fellow, and his recent poems have appeared in *The American Poetry Review, The Believer,* and *The Paris Review.* He is an assistant professor of English and creative writing at the University of San Diego.

Conor Bracken has recent poems appearing in the *Colorado Review, Diode, Indiana Review, The New Yorker,* and elsewhere. He is the author of *Henry Kissinger, Mon Amour* (Bull City Press, 2017), selected by Diane Seuss as winner of the fifth Frost Place Chapbook Competition, and is the translator of Mohammed Khair-Eddine's *Scorpionic Sun* (Cleveland State University Poetry Center, 2019).

Traci Brimhall is the author of *Saudade* (Copper Canyon, 2017), *Our Lady of the Ruins* (W. W. Norton, 2012), and *Rookery* (Southern Illinois University Press, 2010), as well as *Come the Slumberless to* *the Land of Nod* (forthcoming from Copper Canyon, 2020). Her poems have appeared in *The New Yorker, Slate, Poetry, The Believer, The New Republic,* and *Best American Poetry.* A 2013 NEA Fellow, she's currently Director of Creative Writing at Kansas State University.

Stephen Browning's poetry has appeared in *Michigan Quarterly Review, Poetry Northwest, The Southern Review,* and others. This is his second appearance in Ploughshares. He was awarded a Wallace Stegner Fellowship in poetry at Stanford University. A book of his botanical poetry, *Hunger for Light,* was published by the Fithian Press (2015).

Eric Burger has received fellow-ships/awards from the Wisconsin Institute for Creative Writing, the Arizona Commission on the Arts, the Sewanee Writers' Conference, the Wesleyan Writers Conference, and Writers at Work. His poems have appeared in *Denver Quarterly, Black Warrior Review, The Missouri Review Online, Harvard Review Online, Indiana Review, Rattle, Quarterly West, The Southeast Review,* and many others. He is a senior instructor in the University of Colorado-Boulder's Program for Writing and Rhetoric, and lives in Longmont, CO.

Grady Chambers is the author of *North American Stadiums* (Milkweed Editions, 2018), selected by Henri Cole as the winner of the inaugural Max Ritvo Poetry Prize. His poems and stories have appeared in or are forthcoming from *The Paris Review, Kenyon Review Online, Prairie Schooner, Boulevard, Joyland,* and elsewhere. Chambers is a former Wallace Stegner Fellow, and he lives in Philadelphia.

Jim Daniels' most recent books of poems include *Rowing Inland* (Wayne State University Press, 2017) and *Street Calligraphy* (Steel Toe Books, 2017). His sixth book of fiction, *The Perp Walk,* was published by Michigan State University Press in 2019, along with the anthology he edited with M. L. Liebler, *RESPECT: The Poetry of Detroit Music.* He has warmed up for Lucinda Williams, read on *Prairie Home Companion,* had his poem "Factory Love" displayed on a racecar, and is sending poetry to the moon as part of the Moon Arts Project.

Chelsea B. DesAutels' work appears or is forthcoming in *the Missouri Review, Copper Nickel, The Adroit Journal, Pleiades, Willow Springs,* and elsewhere. Natasha Trethewey named Chelsea's manuscript,

Metastasis, the finalist for the AWP Award Series Donald Hall Prize in Poetry. DesAutels received an MFA from the University of Houston, where she served as Poetry Editor of *Gulf Coast*. She lives with her family in Minneapolis.

Daryl Farmer is the author of the nonfiction book *Bicycling Beyond the Divide* (University of Nebraska Press, 2008) and the short-story collection *Where We Land* (Brighthorse Books, 2016). He is an associate professor at the University of Alaska-Fairbanks where he directs the creative-writing program, and is on the faculty of the University of Alaska Anchorage low-residency MFA program.

Owen Good is a translator from the North of Ireland who translates Hungarian poetry and prose. He recently published his debut novel translation: *Pixel* by Krisztina Tóth (Seagull Books, 2019). Good's work has been featured in *Modern Poetry in Translation, Asymptote, World Literature Today, Words Without Borders* and Dalkey Archive's *The Best of European Fiction*. He is coeditor of Hungarian Literature Online.

Gretchen E. Henderson is the author of four books, with the latest translated in 2018 for

Turkish, Korean, Chinese, and Spanish editions. Her essays have appeared in *The Kenyon Review, Brevity, The &NOW Awards: The Best Innovative Writing*, and many other publications. In 2019, her commitments included serving as the Annie Clark Tanner Fellow in Environmental Humanities at the University of Utah, Writer-in-Residence at the Jan Michalski Foundation for Writing and Literature in Switzerland, and Co-Director of a National Endowment for the Humanities Institute on "Museums" at Georgetown University.

Tony Hoagland's book of poems, *Priest Turned Therapist Treats Fear of God*, was published by Graywolf Press in 2018; his craft book, *The Art of Voice: Poetic Principles and Practices*, was published by W.W. Norton in 2019; *The Underground Poetry Metro Transportation System for Souls: Essays on the Cultural Life of Poetry*, was published by the University of Michigan Press in the fall of 2019.

Emily Hoffman's poems have been published by *BOMB, Prodigal, The Threepenny Review*, and *The New Republic*. She is currently pursuing a PhD in Anthropology at Columbia University.

Richie Hofmann is the author of a collection of poems, *Second Empire* (Alice James Books, 2015), winner of the Beatrice Hawley Award from Alice James Books. His poems have appeared recently in *The New Yorker, Poetry, The New York Times Style Magazine*, and *The Baffler*, and have been honored with the Poetry Foundation's Ruth Lilly Fellowship, the Pushcart Prize, and the Wallace Stegner Fellowship, among other prizes. He is currently Jones Lecturer in Poetry at Stanford University.

James Jiang is a writer and academic living in Melbourne, Australia. While his scholarly work focuses on American modernism and philosophical pragmatism, he has written for non-specialist audiences on contemporary poetry, cultures of criticism, and tennis. He is currently working on a book entitled *Sage Modernism* that explores the intersection of pragmatist poetics and therapeutic culture. He is neither waving nor drowning.

Jennifer L. Knox's new collection of poems, *Crushing It*, is forthcoming from Copper Canyon Press in 2020. Her work has appeared four times in *The Best American Poetry* series, and her nonfiction writing has appeared in *The Washington Post* and *The American Poetry Review*. She teaches at Iowa State University and is the proprietor of a small-batch artisanal spice company called Saltlickers.

Keith Leonard is the author of *Ramshackle Ode* (Mariner Books/Houghton Mifflin Harcourt, 2016). He lives in Columbus, Ohio.

Esther Lin was born in Rio de Janeiro, Brazil, and lived in the United States as an undocumented immigrant for twenty-one years. She is a 2020 Writing Fellow at the Fine Arts Work Center in Provincetown, and is the author of *The Ghost Wife*, winner of the 2017 Poetry Society of America Chapbook Fellowship. Her poems have appeared or are forthcoming in *The Indiana Review, The Missouri Review Online, Pleiades, Triquarterly*, and elsewhere. A 2017–2019 Wallace Stegner Fellow, she currently organizes for the Undocupoets.

Kai Maristed is the author of three novels, including *Broken Ground* (Counterpoint, 2003), a Berlin Wall journey, and the story collection *Belong to Me* (starred by *Publisher's Weekly*). Her work has appeared in *Anchor Best Essays, The Kenyon Review, Agni,* and most recently in *The Southwest Review, The Michigan Quarterly,* and *The Iowa Review*. Her translation of Frank Wedekind's *Lulu* is in preproduction in New York. Kai lives in Paris and Boston.

Gail Mazur's collections include *Forbidden City* (University of Chicago Press, 2016); *Figures in a Landscape* (University of Chicago Press, 2011); *Zeppo's First Wife: New and Selected Poems* (University of Chicago Press, 2005), winner of the Massachusetts Book Prize and finalist for *LA Times* Book Prize; and *They Can't Take That Away from Me* (University of Chicago Press, 2001), finalist for the National Book Award. She is founding director of the Blacksmith House Poetry Series in Cambridge, Mass., is on the Writing Committee of the Fine Arts Work Center in Provincetown, and is Visiting Professor in Boston University's MFA Program. *Land's End: New and Selected Poems* is forthcoming in 2020 from University of Chicago Press.

Kerrin McCadden is the author of *Landscape with Plywood Silhouettes,* winner of the New Issues Poetry Prize and the Vermont Book Award (2014); and *Keep This to Yourself,* winner of the Button Poetry Prize (forthcoming). A National Endowment for the Arts Literature Fellow and recipient of the Sustainable Arts Writing Award, her poems have appeared in *Best American Poetry, Poem-a-Day,* and recently in *American Poetry Review, Los Angeles Review, New England Review,* and elsewhere. She lives in South Burlington, Vt.

Amelie Meltzer is a San Francisco native studying in Pittsburgh, PA. She is a medical student and activist working to address racial bias in healthcare and promote the needs of queer and gender-nonconforming patients. She writes poetry and nonfiction. Her writing appears in *New Ohio Review, Roanoke Review, Stoneboat, RipRap,* and *The Hippocrates Prize Anthology.*

Maggie Millner is a poet and teacher from rural upstate New York. Her recent poems have appeared in *The New Yorker, Gulf Coast, The Iowa Review, Freeman's, ZYZZYVA,* and *The Literary Review.* She holds degrees in poetry from New York University and Brown University and currently lives in central Pennsylvania, where she is a 2019–2020 Stadler Fellow at Bucknell University.

Megan Pinto's poetry can be found or is forthcoming in *Meridian, The Cortland Review,* and *Indiana Review.* She has received scholarships from Bread Loaf and the Port Townsend Writer's Conference, and an Amy

Award from *Poets & Writers*. She is a Playmakers Playwright at the Purple Rose Theatre Company, and holds an MFA in Poetry from Warren Wilson.

Catie Rosemurgy is the author of *My Favorite Apocalypse* (Graywolf, 2001) and *The Stranger Manual* (Graywolf, 2010). Her most recent work is a chapbook of poems called *First the Burning* (Bloof Books, 2018.) She's the recipient of a Rona Jaffe Foundation award, a National Endowment for the Arts Fellowship, and a Pew Fellowship in the Arts. She lives in Philadelphia and teaches at The College of New Jersey.

Katherine Sharpe is the author of *Coming of Age on Zoloft* (Harper Perennial, 2012). Her essays and journalism have appeared in *n+1* and other publications. She has a master's degree in literature from Cornell, and is a recent MFA graduate in fiction of The Writing Seminars at Johns Hopkins. She lives with her family in Baltimore, where she is at work on a novel.

Aurelie Sheehan is the author of two novels and four short-story collections, including *Once into the Night*, winner of the 2018 Catherine Doctorow Innovative Fiction Prize (Fiction Collective 2). Her stories have appeared in journals including *Conjunctions, Mississippi Review, New England Review,* and *The Southern Review,* and her novella, *This Blue,* was published as a Ploughshares Solo. Sheehan is a professor and head of the English Department at the University of Arizona.

Claire Sibley's work has recently appeared in *DIAGRAM, FIELD, The Journal,* and *Muzzle Magazine.* Her poems have been semifinalisted and finalisted for the 2018 Nightjar Review Poetry Contest and the Peseroff Prize. Her manuscript, *What the House Made,* was a semifinalist for the 2018 and 2019 Pleiades Press Editors Prizes, and a finalist for the 2019 Lexi Rudnitsky First Book Prize. She holds an MFA from Columbia University and a BA from Middlebury College, and currently lives in Delaware.

Diana Spechler is the author of the novels *Who by Fire* (Harper Perennial, 2008) and S*kinny* (Harper Perennial, 2011) and of the *New York Times* column Going Off. Her work has appeared in *Esquire, Harper's, GQ, Wall Street Journal, Glimmer Train Stories, Playboy, BBC, The Southern Review, Harper's Bazaar,* and many other publications. She has received a number of awards and fellowships, including a Yaddo residency and the Orlando Creative Nonfiction Prize from A Room of Her Own Foundation.

Courtney Faye Taylor is a winner of the 92Y Discovery / Boston Review Poetry Prize and a graduate of the Helen Zell Writers' Program at the University of Michigan. Her poetry appears in *The Kenyon Review*, *The Adroit Journal*, *TriQuarterly*, and elsewhere. Find her online at courtneyfayetaylor.com.

Lynne Thompson is the author of *Start With a Small Guitar* (What Books Press, 2013) and *Beg No Pardon* (Perugia Press, 2007), winner of the Perugia Book Award and the Great Lakes Colleges Association's New Writers Award. In 2018, Jane Hirshfield selected her manuscript *Fretwork* (2019) as the winner of the Marsh Hawk Press Poetry Prize. Recent work appears or is forthcoming in *Poetry, Colorado Review, Nelle, Pleiades,* and *New England Review*, as well as the anthology *Fire and Rain: Ecopoetry of California*.

Sallie Tisdale is the author of nine books and many essays. Her work has appeared in a variety of journals and magazines. Her most recent book is *Advice for Future Corpses*.

Barbara Tran's honors include a MacDowell Colony Fellowship, Pushcart Prize, and Lannan Foundation Writer's Residency. Longlisted for the 2018 CBC Nonfiction Prize, Barbara is indebted to Hedgebrook for radical hospitality at a crucial time, and to the Canada Council for the Arts and the Ontario Arts Council for essential support. Tran's writing has appeared or is forthcoming in *The Puritan, Bennington Review,* and *The New Yorker*.

Daneen Wardrop has authored four books of poetry: *The Odds of Being* (Silverfish Review Press, 2008), *Cyclorama* (Fordham University Press, 2015), *Life as It* (Ashland Poetry Press, 2016), and a 2018 volume, *Silk Road* (Etruscan Press, 2018). She is a recipient of the Independent Publisher Book Award, the National Endowment for the Arts Fellowship, and the Poetry Society of America Robert H. Winner Award. Her work has appeared in *The Iowa Review, AGNI, Virginia Quarterly Review, The Kenyon Review,* and elsewhere. In addition, Wardrop has authored several books of literary criticism, mostly about Emily Dickinson.

Gabriel Welsch's fourth poetry collection is *The Four Horsepersons* of a *Disappointing Apocalypse* (Steel Toe Books, 2013). His fiction and poetry have appeared in journals including *Georgia Review, Southern Review, Mid-American Review, Harvard Review, Missouri Review,* on *Verse Daily,* and in Ted Kooser's column "American Life in Poetry." Recent work appears in *Trampset, Cleaver, Thrush, Ascent,* and *Atticus Review*. He lives in Pittsburgh, Pa., with his family, and is vice president of marketing and communications at Duquesne University.

Jim Whiteside is the author of a chapbook of poems, *Writing Your Name on the Glass* (Bull City Press, 2019). His poems have received support from the Sewanee Writers' Conference, the Virginia Center for the Creative Arts, and the University of North Carolina at Greensboro, where he earned his MFA. Jim's recent poems have appeared in *The Southern Review, Pleiades, Crazyhorse,* and *Washington Square Review*. Originally from Cookeville, Tennessee, he lives in Madison, Wisconsin.

Mark Winegardner's books include the novels *Crooked River Burning* (Houghton Mifflin Harcourt, 2001), *The Veracruz Blues* (Viking Books, 1996), *The Godfather Returns* (Random House, 2004), and *The Godfather's Revenge* (Putnam Books, 2006) as well as the story collection *That's True of Everybody* (Houghton Mifflin Harcourt, 2004). He's now working on a novel called *Florabama Normal*. Winegardner's work has also appeared in *ESPN the Magazine, Esquire, GQ, The New York Times Magazine, Playboy, Five Points, TriQuarterly* and many others. He is the Burroway Chair of English & Distinguished Research Professor at Florida State University.

GUEST EDITOR POLICY

Ploughshares is published four times a year: mixed issues of poetry and prose in the spring and winter, a prose issue in the summer, and a longform prose issue in the fall. The spring and summer issues are guest-edited by different writers of prominence; fall and winter issues are staff-edited. Guest editors are invited to solicit up to half of their issues, with the other half selected from unsolicited manuscripts screened for them by staff editors. This guest editor policy is designed to introduce readers to different literary circles and tastes, and to offer a fuller representation of the range and diversity of contemporary letters than would be possible with a single editorship. Yet, at the same time, we expect every issue to reflect our overall standards of literary excellence.

SUBMISSION POLICIES

We welcome unsolicited manuscripts from June 1 to January 15 (postmark dates). We also accept submissions online. Please see our website (pshares.org/submit) for more information and guidelines. All submissions postmarked from January 16 to May 31 will be recycled or returned unread. From March 1 to May 15, we accept submissions online for our Emerging Writer's Contest.

Our backlog is unpredictable, and staff editors ultimately have the responsibility of determining for which editor a work is most appropriate. If a manuscript is not timely for one issue, it will be considered for another. Unsolicited work sent directly to a guest editor's home or office will be ignored and discarded.

All mailed manuscripts and correspondence regarding submissions should be accompanied by a self-addressed, stamped envelope and email address. Expect three to five months for a decision. We now receive well over a thousand manuscripts a month.

For stories and essays that are significantly longer than 7,500 words, we are now accepting submissions for Ploughshares Solos, which are published as e-books and collected in a longform prose issue in the fall. Pieces for this series, which can be either fiction or nonfiction, can stretch to novella length and range from 7,500 to 20,000 words. The series is edited by Ladette Randolph, Ploughshares Editor-in-chief.

Simultaneous submissions are amenable as long as they are indicated as such and we are notified immediately upon acceptance elsewhere. We do not reprint previously published work. Translations are welcome if permission has been granted. We cannot be responsible for delay, loss, or damage. Payment is upon publication: $45/printed page, $90 minimum and $450 maximum per author, with two copies of the issue and a one-year subscription. For Ploughshares Solos, payment is $450 for long stories and novellas. The prize for our Emerging Writer's Contest is $2,000 for the winner in each genre: fiction, poetry, and nonfiction.

Ploughshares greatly appreciates the support of its patrons. To give your tax-deductible contribution to the Ploughshares Endowed Fund, call us at (617) 824-3753 or visit pshares.org/engage/donate.

.